Coastwise Na...

Notes for Yachtsmen

G G Watkins

Fourth Edition

STANFORD MARITIME

LONDON

Stanford Maritime Limited
Member Company of the George Philip Group
12–14 Long Acre, London WC2E 9LP

First published in Great Britain 1962
Second Edition 1974
Third Edition 1977
Fourth Edition 1984, reprinted 1986
Copyright © Gordon G Watkins 1984

Printed in Great Britain by
Butler & Tanner Ltd, Frome and London

British Library Cataloguing in Publication Data
Watkins, G. G.
   Coastwise Navigation.——4th ed.
   1. Coastwise navigation
   2. Yachts and yachting
   I. Title
   623.89′29   VK559

ISBN 0-540-07282-6

Contents

Preface to the Fourth Edition

This book has been written with the object of introducing coastal navigation to those yachtsmen and women who, so far, have only sailed locally, but now wish to make coastal and short sea passages. It also aims to cover the theoretical parts of the navigation syllabuses for the RYA Day Skipper and Coastal/Offshore Skipper Certificates. It is hoped that it will also serve as an aid to memory to the more experienced yachtsman after his winter 'lay-up'.

The book describes the navigational equipment required and the various factors which should be considered before leaving harbour, as well as during a passage. Whenever appropriate simple drawings and examples have been introduced so that the text can be kept concise and clear.

The metrication of charts and tidal data and the change in European waters to the IALA Buoyage System, Region A, has required changes to the sections on Tides and Navigational Marks, and the acceptance of the Nautical Institute's definitions of Navigational Terms made it necessary to make some changes to Chapter 6. The introduction of VHF Radio Lighthouses, the Coastguard emergency VHF Direction Finding Service and International Port Traffic Signals required additional notes, and numerous other changes have been made to keep the book up to date.

My thanks go to all those people behind the scenes who have helped me in preparing and revising this book.

G.G. Watkins

Acknowledgements

I am indebted to the following manufacturers for the photographs of their yacht equipment:

Offshore Instruments Ltd for their Mini-Compass;

Henry Browne & Son Ltd, for their Sestrel compasses;

Kelvin Hughes Division of Smiths Industries Ltd, for their chartwork instruments;

Seafarer Navigation International Ltd, for their echosounder and radio direction finders;

Lokata Ltd, for their radio direction finders.

I am obliged to the Controller of Her Majesty's Stationery Office and the Hydrographer of the Navy for permission to reproduce portions of Admiralty charts and publications including extracts from Tide Tables, and also to Messrs. Thomas Reed Publications Ltd. for permission to reproduce portions of Reed's Nautical Almanac.

G.G.W.

Chapter 1

An Introduction to Charts

Navigation is the science of finding a boat's position at sea, and of directing her safely from one place to another.

A knowledge of charts, Sailing Directions (known as 'Pilots'), Light Lists, and other publications is required, as well as other aids such as buoys, lighthouses, lights, fog signals and radiobeacons.

So that these aids may be used in navigating a boat, their positions on the earth's surface must be known. It is therefore necessary to know something about the earth, and the method adopted to define position on the earth's surface, together with the units of measurement used.

THE EARTH is not a perfect sphere, but may be considered so for most practical purposes in navigation without appreciable error.

DIRECTION. The direction towards which the earth rotates is called East. This is the cardinal point on that side of the horizon where the heavenly bodies rise. The opposite cardinal point is called West. The end of the earth's axis of rotation which lies on the left of an observer facing east is known as the North Pole. The opposite end of the earth's axis of rotation is known as the South Pole.

POSITION. The position of any place is given by stating its latitude and longitude in degrees (°), minutes ('), and seconds ("). (There are 90 degrees in one right angle, 60 minutes make one degree, and 60 seconds make one minute.)

The *latitude* of a place is its angular distance from the equator measured along its meridian of longitude from 0° to 90° north or south.

The *longitude* of a place is its angular distance from the Greenwich meridian measured along the equator from 0° to 180° east or west (see Fig. 1.1).

For example, the position of North Foreland lighthouse is:
51 degrees 22 minutes 28 seconds North, 1 degree 26 minutes 49 seconds East. This is written: 51° 22' 28" N, 1° 26' 49" E.

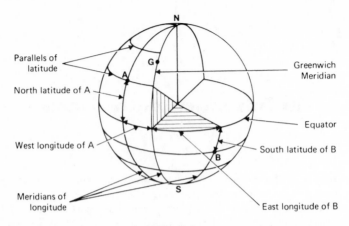

Fig. 1.1

When the different convention of stating positions in degrees, minutes and tenths of minutes is used, the accepted notation is, for example, 46°01′.5N (46 degrees 1½ minutes) although the alternative style 46° 01·5′N is sometimes seen in nautical publications.

Units of Distance

THE STATUTE MILE is an arbitrary unit and has no connection with any length on the earth's surface. Its length was laid down by Statute in the reign of Queen Elizabeth I as being '8 furlongs of 40 perches of 16½ feet each' giving a length of 5280 feet.

THE NAUTICAL OR SEA MILE is the unit used at sea and is approximately the distance in feet, measured along a meridian, separating two places whose latitude differs by one minute. Because the earth is not exactly spherical, this length varies from 6046 feet at the Equator to 6108 feet at the poles, the mean being 6077 feet. For convenience a length of 6080 feet is used. The International nautical mile is 1852 metres.

Other Units used in Navigation

A FATHOM equals 6 feet or 2 yards.

A METRE is approximately 3·3 feet and a DECIMETRE, which is one-tenth of a metre, is approximately 4 inches.

A CABLE equals one-tenth part of a nautical mile or 608 feet (approximately 200 yards or 100 fathoms).

A KNOT is the unit of speed and is equal to 1 nautical mile per hour.

Charts

A chart is a map used by a navigator. The navigable sea areas of the world and the adjacent coastlines are depicted on charts, the detail shown depending upon the scale to which the chart is drawn.

When a large area of the earth's surface is represented, the chart is a *Small Scale Chart*. These are used mainly for sea or ocean crossings to enable the navigator to plot his position and plan his route. Only the more important lighthouses and radio aids to navigation are marked upon the coastline shown, as a *Large Scale Chart* should be used when approaching the land.

A large scale chart shows a much smaller area of the earth's surface in great detail, and indicates the nature of the coastline, depths of water up to the coast, important land features visible from the sea, lighthouses and floating marks such as buoys and lightvessels, which may be used by the navigator. Information about tidal streams is shown, and also all dangers to navigation such as rocks, shoals, wrecks, etc that must be avoided.

The natural scale of a chart is marked on it in the 'legend' under its title, and is the ratio that a length measured on the chart bears to the corresponding length measured on the earth's surface, for example:

On a small scale chart, 1/500,000 means that one inch on the chart represents 500,000 inches or 6·85 miles on the earth's surface, i.e. 0·15in to 1 mile. On a large scale chart, 1/36,500 means one inch on the chart represents 36,500 inches or 0·5 mile on the earth's surface, i.e. 2in to 1 mile.

The Hydrographic Department of the Admiralty is the largest and most important publisher of charts in the United Kingdom. It publishes charts of all parts of the world, which are obtainable from Admiralty Chart Agents situated at more than 90 ports in the British Isles, and also at the principal ports of the world. A list of these agents is published annually in Admiralty Notice to Mariners No. 2.

To enable the necessary charts for a passage to be selected, a full catalogue of charts and publications is published by the Hydrographic Department and it may be seen at chart agents. A Home Edition of this catalogue for the use of coastal shipping and yachtsmen is also published. It lists charts and publications relating to the British Isles and NW Europe from Brest to Denmark, and shows on Index charts the area covered by each individual chart.

Charts are also published by Imray, Laurie, Norie & Wilson Ltd, and Stanford Charts by Barnacle Marine Ltd. These are obtainable from most chart agents and yacht chandlers. They are drawn with the yachtsman in mind, and they make more use of colours to present information than is done on Admiralty charts. They may often be more economical than Admiralty charts as, on a number of them, plans of ports marked on the main part of the chart are shown, drawn to a larger scale, as insets to the main chart. These plans will not show as much detail or be drawn to as large a scale as the equivalent Admiralty plan, but they are often sufficient for navigating a small vessel into port, particularly so in the case of Stanford's charts which also print pilotage and other information on the back of the chart.

Several different projections are used by map makers in order to depict the curved surface of the earth on a flat piece of paper, and each distorts the actual area shown in one way or another. The most useful chart for a navigator is one upon which he can draw a straight line joining his starting point to his destination, and then obtain by measurement the direction in which to head his vessel. The Mercator projection, which is mathematically constructed, allows him to do this.

THE MERCATOR CHART On a Mercator chart the Equator and all parallels of latitude shown are straight lines parallel to each other. The meridians are straight lines drawn at right angles to the parallels and the Equator and spaced an equal distance apart. As the meridians on the earth's surface converge towards the Poles, the above method of drawing the meridians, causes distortion of land masses in an east-west direction. To preserve the correct shape of the land, the parallels of latitude, which are equally spaced on the earth, are drawn in on the chart an increasing distance apart, as the latitude increases towards the Poles.

The distance between two points is measured by using the latitude scale at the sides of the chart, as 1 minute of latitude is equal to 1 nautical mile. Since each minute of latitude as marked on the chart gets progressively longer towards the Poles, it is important that only that part of the latitude scale is used which lies abreast of the two points whose distance apart is required. The longitude scale at the top and bottom edges is never used to measure distance.

Examples of the latitude scales on Admiralty charts are shown in Fig. 1.2.

GNOMONIC PROJECTION Port approach and harbour charts are drawn on the gnomonic projection, as are certain special charts for ocean navigation and charts of polar regions.

On a gnomonic chart, meridians appear as straight lines converging to the Poles and parallels of latitude are curves.

On the large scale charts of small areas in the approaches to ports, etc the curvature of the parallels, and convergence of the meridians,

**METHODS OF GRADUATING LATITUDE SCALES
ON ADMIRALTY CHARTS**

Fig. 1.2

is so slight that the chart may be used in the same manner as any other chart. Distance may be measured either by using the latitude scale as is done on the Mercator chart, or from a separate scale of distance that is marked at the bottom or side of this type of chart. Large scale gnomonic charts of port approaches, etc are graduated as shown in Fig. 1.2.

METRIC CHARTS The Hydrographer of the Navy has started a long-term programme of converting Admiralty navigational charts to metric units. The first metric charts of British Isles waters were published in 1972, and the conversion for those waters had largely been completed by 1983. The whole programme is a major task and this will necessarily mean that for many years both fathoms and metric charts of some areas will continue to be published. Metric charts are easily recognised by the greater use of colour, and by the words DEPTHS IN METRES clearly marked in magenta.

SYMBOLS AND ABBREVIATIONS are used on charts to present as much information as possible in the smallest space. Most symbols and abbreviations used on Admiralty charts are common to metric

SYMBOLS AND ABBREVIATIONS FROM ADMIRALTY CHART No. 5011 (BOOK EDITION)

The Coastline
Metric Charts

1 Coast imperfectly known or shoreline unsurveyed	1 1b Foreshore, Sand
2 Steep coast	11a Foreshore, Mud
3 Cliffy coast	11c Foreshore, Stones, Gravel and Shingle
4 Sand dunes	11d Foreshore, Rock
5 Stony or shingly shore	11e Foreshore, Sand and Mud
6 Sandy shore	11f Foreshore, Sand and Gravel
8 Surveyed coastline	(Aa) Limiting danger line
10 Low Water Line	12 Breakers along a shore

Topography
Metric Charts

1 Contour lines	1a Contour lines, approximate

Dangers
Metric Charts

1 Rock which does not cover (with elevation above MHWS or MHHW, or where there is no tide, above MSL)	12 Wreck of which the masts only are visible — (Masts) (Mast 3m) (Funnel) (Mast dries 2·1m) Large scale charts
2 §Rock which covers and uncovers (with elevation above chart datum)	(Oa) Unsurveyed wreck over which the exact depth is unknown but which is considered to have a safe clearance at the depth shown
3 Rock awash at the level of chart datum	
4 Sunken rock with ·2 metres or less water over it at chart datum, or rock ledge on which depths are known to be 2 metres or less, or a rock or rock ledge over which the exact depth is unknown but which is considered to be dangerous to surface navigation	14 Wreck over which the exact depth of water is unknown but is thought to be 28 metres or less, and which is considered dangerous to surface navigation
5 Shoal sounding on isolated rock	15 ‡Wreck over which the depth has been obtained by sounding, but not by wire sweep
6 Sunken rock not dangerous to surface navigation	15a ‡Wreck which has been swept by wire to the depth shown
6a Sunken danger with depth cleared by wire drag	16 ‡Wreck over which the exact depth is unknown but thought to be more than 28 metres, or a wreck over which the depth is thought to be 28 metres or less, but which is not considered dangerous to surface vessels capable of navigating in the vicinity.
19 Eddies	
38 Limiting danger line	17 The remains of a wreck, or other foul area, no longer dangerous to surface navigation, but to be avoided by vessels anchoring, trawling, etc.
11 Wreck showing any portion of hull or superstructure at the level of chart datum — Large scale charts	18 Overfalls and tide-rips

Reproduced from British Admiralty Chart No. 5011 with the permission of the Controller of H.M. Stationery Office and of the Hydrographer of the Navy.

Fig. 1.3

Reproduced from British Admiralty Chart No. 5011 with the permission of the Controller of H.M. Stationery Office and of the Hydrographer of the Navy.

Fig. 1.3a

and fathoms charts, and users should have little difficulty in transferring from one type of chart to the other. They are shown on chart No. 5011, which is published in the form of a booklet, and are also printed in Reed's Nautical Almanac. A selection of the more important symbols and abbreviations together with their meanings is given in Fig. 1.3 and 1.3a. By international agreement, the same or related symbols are used on many foreign charts.

Notices to Mariners

New information is constantly being received at the Admiralty about the navigable sea areas of the world. To enable this information to be passed on to the navigator so that he may keep his charts and publications up to date, the Admiralty publishes Notices to Mariners in the form of a weekly booklet, which may be seen or obtained free from Admiralty Chart Agents, Customs Houses, Harbour Authorities and Mercantile Marine Officers. Many chart agents will correct charts on payment of a fee. A Small Craft Edition containing collected Notices for the British Isles and European coast from the Gironde to the Elbe can be purchased quarterly.

Number of notice, which should be put
at bottom left hand corner of chart
after information has been inserted.

*367.   ENGLAND, South Coast — Chichester Harbour Entrance—Shoal depths.

(1) Depths are to be inserted as follows:—

Depth	Position
(a) 0_6 metres	50° 45'·08 N., 0° 56'·35 W.
(b) 0_7 metres	50° 45'·26 N., 0° 56'·15 W.
(c) 0_6 metres	50° 45'·74 N., 0° 56'·58 W.
(d) Dries 0_3 metres, surrounded by a contour line	50° 45'·82 N., 0° 56'·09 W.

(2) The 2 metre contour is to be amended to pass S. and close E. of (1d).

(3) The following depths are to be deleted:—

Depth	Approximate Position
(a) 1_8 metres	close S.S.W. of (1a)
(b) 1 metre	close W. of (1c)

Charts [*Last correction*].—**2050** & **L(D1)** 2050 [*2406/82*]—**3418** [*2406/82*]—**2045**
& **L(D1)** 2045 (1a) [*2717/82*].
H.M. Surveying Ship *Herald*.   (*H. 2038/82.*)

One of Decca
charts affected

Last Notice
affecting chart 2045

One of
charts
affected

Part of Notice that
affects chart 2045 and
L(D1) 2045

Fig. 1.4   Example of a Notice to Mariners

Chapter 2

Navigational Marks

Lights

The abbreviations given on chart 5011 and Lists of Lights to describe the lights shown from lighthouses, beacons, lightvessels and buoys require some explanation and this is given in the following notes.

The position of a lighthouse or light beacon is indicated by a star as follows ✪ or ✳ . This is further emphasised on the chart by over-printing with a magenta 'splash' or 'flare'.

A light is described by giving:
1. Its distinguishing appearance (characteristic)
2. Colour
3. Time required for one complete cycle (period)
4. Elevation ⎱ not given for light buoys.
5. Range in clear weather ⎰

CHARACTERISTICS used to distinguish lights, with their abbreviations (older form in *italics*).

F	**Fixed.** A continuous steady light.
Fl	**Flashing.** A single flash at regular intervals, or a steady light with regular intervals of total darkness; in each case, the duration of *light* is always *less* than that of darkness.
Fl (2) *Gp. Fl. (2)*	**Group Flashing.** A group of two or more flashes at regular intervals. Some lights show alternate groups with a different number of flashes, e.g. $(2+3)$.
Oc *Occ*	**Occulting.** A steady light with sudden and regular intervals of darkness. Duration of *light* is always *more* than that of darkness.
Iso	**Isophase.** Light showing equal intervals of light and darkness.
Mo. (K)	**Morse Code.** Light showing long and short flashes grouped to form Morse letters or numbers (in this example, the letter K — · —).

9

Oc (2) **Group Occulting.** A steady light with a group of two
Gp. Occ. (2) or more (two in this example) regular intervals of
darkness. At some lights alternate groups are different
in number, e.g. (1 + 3).

F Fl **Fixed and Flashing.** A fixed light varied at regular
intervals by a single flash of relatively greater brilli-
ance.

Q (3) **Group Quick Flashing.** A light which flashes at a
Gp. Qk. Fl. (3) rate of fifty or more times a minute in groups (here, of
three).

Q **Quick Flashing.** A light which flashes continuously
Qk. Fl. at fifty or more times a minute.

IQ **Interrupted Quick Flashing.** A light which flashes
Int. Qk. Fl. at a rate of more than fifty times a minute, with a
regular interval of total darkness.

A number, or numbers, in brackets after the abbreviations Fl, Q
and Oc denote the number of flashes and intervals of darkness respectively in each group. Letters or numbers in brackets following the
abbreviation Mo. indicate the Morse Code characters formed by the
long and short flashes.

COLOUR The abbreviations used to indicate the colour of the light
exhibited are as follows: Bu ... Blue; G ... Green; Y ... Yellow or
Orange; R ... Red; Vi ... Violet; W ... White.

A light which has no colour abbreviation after its characteristic
exhibits a white light and no other, although another separate and
distinct coloured light may be shown from a different part of the same
lighthouse, thus the description of the lights shown from the Skerries
lighthouse off Anglesey is Fl.(2)10s.36m. 29M & FR26m.16M. This
indicates that groups of 2 white flashes are exhibited every 10 seconds
from a height of 36 metres, and a second continuous red light is shown
from a height of 26 metres in the same tower. The second light, as in
the example described above, usually shows over a narrow sector in
order to indicate a dangerous line of approach.

Certain lights show different colours in succession. Their characteristics are preceded by the abbreviation Al (meaning alternating) and
followed by the colours shown. The sequence of colours indicated will
be seen from any part of the visible sector covered by the light.

Wolf Rock lighthouse off Lands End shows all round the horizon in
each cycle: a 0·7 sec. white flash; 14·3 sec. darkness; a 0·7 sec. red flash;
14·3 sec. darkness.

Its description on the chart is AlFlWR30s (previously *Alt. Fl. W.R. 30 sec*).

Other lights change colour in sectors, usually to indicate either a safe approach sector, or alternatively a sector or sectors which cover some unmarked dangers, e.g. Longships lighthouse off Lands End shows a white and a red light for 5 seconds and then darkness for 5 seconds in each cycle.

The white light is shown over a 222° sector to seaward, and the red

Fig. 2.1   Longships Light-Sectors

light is shown over a 19° sector northward, and a 20° sector south-eastward, from the lighthouse as shown in Fig. 2.1. The two red sectors cover off-lying rocks and dangers off the coast. The abridged description of the light shown on the chart of this area is IsoWR10s35m19,18M. The sectors are only marked as shown in the figure on large scale charts. If a large scale chart is not available, reference should be made to the Light List for the area or to Reed's Nautical Almanac. It is important to note the difference between the two types of lights just described. In the case of Wolf Rock light a vessel would see *both* the white and red lights alternately, even if she were stopped. A vessel stopped to seaward of Longships light in the white sector would *only* see a white light, and she would have to *move* into either of the red sectors in order to see the red light.

PERIOD The period of a light is the time required to complete one cycle of the characteristic, i.e. from the instant when the characteristic starts to the instant when the characteristic next starts, including any intervening darkness.

For example:

Bishop Rock light shows a white light in each cycle, as follows:

flash 0·3 sec.; darkness 1·6 sec.; flash 0·3 sec.; darkness 12·8 sec.

Its period is therefore 15 seconds and its description, as marked on the chart is Fl.(2)15s (previously *Gp. Fl. (2)15sec*).

The Needles light shows a white, red and green light over sectors in its period of 20 seconds as follows:

light 14 sec.; darkness 2 sec.; light 2 sec.; darkness 2 sec.

The abridged description on the chart is Oc(2)WRG20s (previously *Gp. Occ. (2) WRG 20 sec*).

It is important on first sighting a light to note its characteristic by carefully counting the number of flashes or intervals of darkness. The period should then be checked by counting or by stopwatch. If an observer starts to count at the beginning of each cycle as follows:

'and one and two and three and four and five and six etc. . . .'

until the cycle begins again, a good estimate of the period can be obtained. (This method of counting can be practised at any time against a watch to obtain an even rate.) The chart should then be examined and the light identified. When expecting to sight a light, it should not be assumed, when one is sighted, that it is the expected light until the check described above has been carried out. A stop watch is ideal for timing lights.

ELEVATION The elevation of a light given on the chart is measured in metres (or feet on fathoms charts) between the focal plane of the light and the tidal levels Mean High Water Springs (MHWS) or Mean Higher High Water (MHHW) or, where there is no tide, Mean Sea Level (MSL). (See Chapter 3 for MHWS.)

THE RANGE of a light given on a chart published before 31 March 1972 is the lesser of the Geographical and Luminous ranges. All new charts and new editions published on or after the above date will give the Nominal range which is the range when the meteorological visibility is 10 sea miles, and takes account of the intensity of the light. The Geographical range assumed the observer's eye was 15 feet or 5 metres above the sea. It takes account of refraction and curvature of the earth, while Luminous range is the maximum distance the light can be seen taking into account the meteorological visibility and the intensity of the light.

When passing close to a flashing light, a faint continuous light may be seen between the flashes.

Lights are exhibited at least from sunset to sunrise and during foggy or hazy weather from before sunset to after sunrise. Lights under the jurisdiction of the Clyde Lighthouse Trust are shown during the day in fog.

Other Abbreviations Used to Describe Lights
Aero Lights marked on a chart with the word 'Aero' placed before the characteristic are primarily for the use of aircraft, but may be visible from the sea. They are often of great luminous power and elevation, and on some coasts may be the first lights sighted when approaching the coast. These lights often have characteristics similar to ordinary navigational lights, but others flash single letter or two-letter Morse groups in various colours. The letter or letters shown are indicated in the characteristic marked on the chart or in the Light List; for example Aero Mo(AB); or Aero AltFlWG. Such lights should be used with caution as they are subject to changes which may not always be promptly notified to the mariner.

Leading or **Ldg** is marked against two lights which, when in line, act as leading lights in a channel or into a harbour. On large scale charts such lights will be shown as follows:

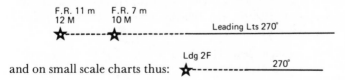

F.R. 11 m   F.R. 7 m
12 M   10 M
                                    Leading Lts 270°

and on small scale charts thus:
Ldg 2F
270°

13

Lights described as **Lts in line** are intended to mark limits of areas, alignments for anchoring, etc.; they do not mark a direction to be followed.

The solid line, as shown above, indicates the advised safe limit of approach to the leading lights, the dotted portion of the line being drawn to guide the eye to the lights which are to be kept in line, the figures indicating their true direction when in line. The rear light (that furthest from the vessel when on the leading line) is always placed higher than the front light, so that when in line they appear vertically one above the other.

Leading lights as seen from a boat.

Aerial view of leads shown above.

View (a): lights in line, boat correctly on leading line.

View (b): front light to the right of rear light. Boat is therefore to the left of the leading line, and should steer to the right until (a) is achieved.

View (c): front light to the left of rear light. Boat is therefore to the right of the leading line, and should steer to the left until (a) is achieved.

It will be seen from the above that if a boat is steering along the leading line, and the front light appears to move to the right, she steers to the right to regain the line. If the front light appears to move to the left, she steers to the left to regain the line. In other words she 'follows' the front light or lead.

Dir. A single leading light with a narrow sector or narrow intensified arc.

Obscd. Light obscured in sector indicated.

(occas) Occasional. Marked against lights that are only exhibited when a vessel is expected, or at other irregular times.

(vert) Lights placed vertically.

(hor) Lights placed horizontally.

Fog Det Lt Marked against lighthouses which are fitted with fog detector lights, additional to the main light, for the automatic detection of fog. These lights sweep back and forth along the sea horizon, first in one direction and then in the other, exhibiting a powerful bluish flash of about one second duration. The period between flashes will vary with the position of the vessel within the arc of visibility. At the limits of the arc of visibility the duration of the flash may be considerably longer than one second. At present only a few lighthouses in the British Isles and Norway are fitted with these lights.

Light Structures

Lights are exhibited from structures which vary in size and construction, from tall stone towers with living accommodation for keepers down to small latticework structures built of steel angles, from which lights operate automatically. Each structure is made as conspicuous as possible against its particular background so that it may be more easily identified by day when viewed from offshore. They are often white or grey, occasionally marked with a contrasting dark band or bands, or alternatively red or black, with occasionally a contrasting white band or bands. Other colours may be used if necessary. The height of the structure may often be appreciably less than the charted elevation of the light, particularly when it is built on a cliff top. Thus Anvil Point lighthouse consists of a white tower 12 metres high but placed so that the light is exhibited from an elevation of 45 metres above MHWS. Because of this, during daylight hours a boat has to be appreciably closer to a lighthouse to identify, and make use of it, than she has to be at night when the light is exhibited.

A brief description of each lighthouse is given in the Light Lists, and 'Pilot' for the particular areas involved, and in briefer form in nautical almanacs.

Lightvessels

These are marked on charts by the symbol , the small circle at the centre of the base indicating the exact position. The colour of the lightvessel is marked beneath the symbol as shown. Descriptions of all lightvessels, both British and foreign, are found in the relevant Light Lists and Sailing Directions.

Those situated near the coasts of the British Isles are painted red, and their names are painted in large white letters on each side. Some Continental lightvessels are red, with white vertical stripes or white bands.

Lightvessels are placed off coasts where there are shoals extending or lying some way offshore, and also in wide river estuaries where the main channels lie too far from the coasts for shore lights to be of assistance, as in the Thames Estuary. Lightvessels exhibit lights with distinctive characteristics similar to those previously described, and the same abbreviations are used on charts to describe them.

A white riding light is shown forward on the forestay, 2 metres above the rail, and this when visible indicates the direction in which the lightvessel is swung to her mooring, and also gives some indication of the direction of the tidal stream at that position at the time. If a strong wind is blowing this method of estimating the direction of the tidal stream should not be relied upon, as the wind may cause the lightvessel to lie across the stream.

If at any time a lightvessel cannot show the characteristic light while she is on station, only the riding light on the forestay will be shown.

Other signals that may be shown from lightvessels are listed in full in the relevant Light List and in Reed's Nautical Almanac.

It should be borne in mind that lightvessels may be withdrawn for repairs without notice, and temporarily replaced by a relief vessel or light buoy exhibiting a different characteristic light.

Large Automatic Navigation Buoys (Lanby)

Some Trinity House lightvessels will be replaced over the next few years by this new type of buoy. A *Lanby* is a discus shaped steel buoy 12 metres in diameter, 2 metres deep, and fitted with a central tubular mast superstructure 12 metres high which houses the high-power light. These buoys are fitted with electric fog signals having a range of approximately 3 miles, and they can be fitted with radiobeacons and racons if required. The equipment on a *Lanby* is controlled and monitored from a shore station or light tower nearby over a radio link.

Fig. 2.2   Lanby

Movable Drilling Rigs and Permanent Platforms

These may be encountered anywhere in the waters surrounding the British Isles and NW Europe. A rig indicates its position by exhibiting a white light flashing the Morse letter U every 15 seconds visible 15 miles, and red lights flash U every 15 seconds from the extremities visible 3 miles. In fog the Morse signal U is sounded by a horn every 30 seconds.

Note that these structures may be either self-propelled or towed. In the latter case the towlines will be long and the tugs some distance away. When under way, the normal lights for towing or self-propulsion are displayed.

Fog Signals

During fog, many lighthouses, lightvessels and buoys, make fog signals at regular intervals. Mariners are warned that fog signals must never be relied on implicitly as sound is conveyed in a very irregular way through the atmosphere: the following points should be borne in mind. Fog signals are heard at greatly varying distances and there may be areas around a station in which the signal is inaudible. Fog may exist a short distance from a station but may not be seen from it, so that the signal may not be sounded, and some emitters cannot be started immediately signs of fog are seen. One of the tones of a fog signal which is a combination of high and low tones may be inaudible under certain atmospheric conditions.

The abbreviations and descriptions of various types of signal are set out below.

Dia   A diaphone generally emits a powerful low-pitched sound which often ends with brief sound of suddenly lowered pitch which sounds like and is called the 'grunt'.

Siren   A compressed air siren, of which there are many different types which differ considerably in their sound and power.

Reed   A reed uses compressed air and emits a weak, high-pitched sound.

Explos   An explosive emitter produces short reports by firing explosive charges.

Horn   Fog horns use compressed air or electricity to vibrate a diaphragm. There are a number of types which differ greatly in their sound and power. Some, particularly those at main fog signal stations, combine simultaneously produced sounds of different pitch, to emit a very powerful signal. Others produce a single steady note, while others vary continuously in pitch.

Bell   The bell, the gong and the whistle may be operated by
Gong   machinery, sounding a regular character; by hand, sound-
Whis   ing somewhat irregularly; or by wave action, sounding erratically.

The obsolescent abbreviations Tyfon and E.F. Horn which may be seen on fathoms charts sound like the Horn described above, while a Nauto, short for nautophone, sounds like a Reed. Fog signals with Morse or composite characteristics are abbreviated in a similar manner to lights, e.g. Horn Mo(U); Siren(1 + 2).

Other Floating Marks

The edges of shoals and deep water channels in rivers and into harbours, and isolated dangers such as rocks and wrecks, are usually marked by coloured buoys or floats kept in position by heavy sinkers on the sea bed. They are made of steel in distinctive shapes and painted a distinctive colour or colours, to indicate by day what they mark, and which side they should be passed to avoid danger. Many buoys have a further distinctive shape, known as a topmark, fitted above the main structure to help identification. Most buoys are named or numbered, and these names or numbers are marked on the side of the main structure.

In channels and areas used regularly by day and night, buoys and floats are fitted with automatic white or coloured lights with distinc-

Left: conical buoy and single topmark. Right: can buoys and topmark.

tive characteristics, to enable them to be identified and to indicate which side they should be passed. In secondary and little used channels buoys may not be fitted with lights, and also they may be withdrawn during the winter months. To assist ships with radar, most major buoys in main channels are fitted with radar reflectors so that they show more clearly on a radar screen and at a greater range. Before 1977 the symbol ⌁ was marked on charts above the position of any mark fitted with a radar reflector, but this practice is discontinued for IALA System marks. Radar reflectors must not be confused with topmarks. Floating marks are sometimes temporarily driven from their charted positions in bad weather, and a boat's position should be checked by other means when possible.

To obtain information about a particular buoy or buoys, the largest scale chart of the area should be examined. The Sailing Directions and nautical almanacs give some information about buoys, but the Light Lists include only a very few.

For many years, two separate systems of buoyage were used off the coasts of the British Isles and NW Europe. One, the Lateral System, used to mark long narrow channels; the other, the Cardinal System, generally to mark isolated rocks and shoals. Starting in 1977, the International Association of Lighthouse Authorities (IALA) introduced into European waters a new system called the IALA Maritime Buoyage System. It uses Red to Port, in Region A which includes Europe, Australia, New Zealand, Africa, the Gulf, and some Asian countries. In North, Central and South America, Japan, Korea and the Philippines, known as Region B, the buoyage rule is Red to Starboard.

IALA Maritime Buoyage System
The System applies to all fixed beacons and floating marks, other than lighthouses, sector lights, leading lights, lightvessels and Lanbys. Most

lighted and unlighted beacons, other than leading marks, are included. Because of the variety of beacon structures used, the shape and colour of a beacon's topmark will usually indicate the desired navigational information.

There are five types of marks used in combination, of which **Lateral** marks indicate the port and starboard hand sides of defined channels, with a modified Lateral mark indicating a preferred route when a channel divides.

Cardinal marks indicate the side that navigable water lies by reference to the compass, while **Isolated Danger** marks are erected on or moored over dangers of limited extent. **Safe Water** marks such as mid-channel buoys and **Special** marks, where reference to the chart is required, complete the available types.

Direction of buoyage Lateral marks indicate the port and starboard hand sides of channels to be followed in conjunction with a

Fig. 2.7a Left: symbol used to indicate buoyage direction on charts. Right: general direction of buoyage around the British Isles.

Fig. 2.7b The General direction gives way to the Local direction at the outer limit of the Thames Estuary.

conventio ıal direction of buoyage. This is either the **Local direction**, which is that taken by the mariner when approaching a harbour, river, estuary or other waterway from seaward, or the **General direction** of buoyage, decided by the buoyage authorities, which follows a clockwise direction around continental land masses and is usually given in Sailing Directions, and if necessary indicated on charts by the arrow symbol in Figs. 2.7a/b.

The General Direction of Buoyage around the British Isles runs northward along the west coasts and through the Irish Sea, eastward along the English Channel and northward through the North Sea (Fig. 2.7a). The General Direction gives way to the Local Direction at the outer limits of the Thames Estuary (Fig. 2.7b).

MARKS USED IN IALA REGION A

Readers may find it useful to colour in the diagrams of marks, following the colour descriptions given next to each one. Black topmarks and bands are printed solid black, and the white or shaded areas can be coloured in red, green or yellow as appropriate.

STARBOARD HAND marks are to be kept on the mariner's right hand when proceeding in the direction of buoyage.

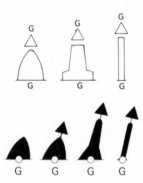

Buoys are Green, conical or pillar or pillar or spar shape, and may be fitted with a Green conical topmark, point up. A Green light showing any rhythm except Fl(2+1)G may be exhibited. Beacons are generally Green, with a Green cone topmark, point up.

Chart symbols

PORT HAND marks are to be kept on the mariner's left hand when proceeding in the direction of the buoyage.

Buoys are Red, can or pillar or spar shape, and may be fitted with a Red can topmark. A Red light showing any rhythm except Fl(2+1)R may be exhibited.
Beacons are generally Red, with a Red can topmark.

Chart symbols

PREFERRED CHANNELS When proceeding in the direction of buoyage, a preferred channel may be indicated at a point where the channel divides by a modified starboard or port hand lateral mark.

PREFERRED CHANNEL TO PORT (Leave to starboard)

Green conical, pillar or spar buoy with one broad red horizontal band. Green cone topmark (if any). A green light Fl(2 + 1)G may be shown.

GRG

Chart symbol solid black conical buoy

PREFERRED CHANNEL TO STARBOARD (Leave to port)

Red can, pillar or spar buoy with one broad green horizontal band. Red can topmark (if any). A red light Fl(2 + 1)R may be shown.

RGR

Chart symbol black outlined can buoy

CARDINAL MARKS may be used to indicate that the deepest water in an area is on the named side of the mark; to indicate the safe side on which to pass a danger; or to draw attention to a feature in a channel such as a bend, junction, fork or end of a shoal.

Such a mark is placed in one of the four quadrants North, East, South and West from the point of interest, and takes its name from the quadrant in which it is placed. The mariner is safe if he passes N of a North mark, E of an East mark, and so on.

The shape of a cardinal mark is not important, but buoys are pillar or spar shape, and always fitted, when practicable, with black vertical double cone topmarks, the arrangement of which is important and should be memorised. When lighted, a white Quick Flashing or Very Quick Flashing light is exhibited. Quick Flashing (Q) lights flash at the rate of 60 or 50 flashes per minute; a Very Quick Flashing (VQ) light at double that rate. A Long Flash (L Fl) is a flash of not less than 2 seconds' duration. The exact rhythm which identifies the quadrant is shown in Fig. 2.8.

CARDINAL MARKS

Topmarks are always fitted (when practicable)

Buoy shapes are pillar or spar

Lights, when fitted, are **white** Very Quick Lights or Quick Lights; a South mark also has a Long Flash immediately following the quick flashes.

Fig. 2.8   Cardinal marks

Chart symbols used for cardinal buoys, and colour markings, are shown and described below.

North Marks, to be passed on their North side, have two black cones points up, and are painted with a black band above a yellow band (BY). A white Quick Flashing or Very Quick Flashing light may be shown.

BY   BY

East Marks, to be passed on their East side, have two black cones points outward, and are painted with black bands above and below a yellow band (BYB). A white light showing groups of 3 Quick or Very Quick Flashes may be exhibited.

BYB   BYB

South Marks, to be passed on their South side, have two black cones points down, and are painted with a black band below a yellow band (YB). A white light showing groups of 6, Quick or Very Quick Flashes followed by a Long Flash, may be shown. (The Long Flash is to ensure that the 6 flashes are not mistaken for the groups of 3 or 9 flashes shown by East and West marks.)

YB   YB

West Marks, to be passed on their West side, have two black cones points inward, and are painted with a black band with yellow bands above and below (YBY). A white light showing groups of 9, Quick or Very Quick Flashes, may be exhibited.

YBY   YBY

To aid memory, the number of flashes can be related to a clock face, where 3 o'clock is E, 6 o'clock S and 9 o'clock W; also the West topmarks look like a Wineglass, and the East ones form an Egg shape. The black part of the buoy or beacon corresponds to the points of the topmarks, e.g. black over yellow (BY) on North marks, in the middle between the yellow bands (YBY) on West marks, and at the top and bottom (BYB) on East marks.

ISOLATED DANGER MARKS are erected on, or moored above isolated rocks or shoals which have deep water all round them. The position of a buoy marking such a danger is shown on the chart slightly to one side of the danger.

Isolated Danger

BRB   BRB

A mark is painted with Red and Black horizontal bands, and if a buoy, is pillar or spar shape. The topmark, consisting of two black spheres one above the other, is fitted whenever practicable, and is the most important feature of this mark. A white light showing 2 flashes may be shown.

Chart symbols

SAFE WATER MARKS are used to indicate that there is navigable water all round the mark. Several of them in a line may be used to define the centreline of a channel. A single buoy might be used as a landfall buoy.

Safe Water Mark

RW   RW   RW

Buoys are spherical, pillar or spar shape, painted with Red and White vertical stripes. A red sphere topmark will normally be fitted on pillar or spar buoys. A white Occulting, Isophase, Long Flashing or Morse A ($\cdot\ -$) light may be shown.

Chart symbols

SPECIAL MARKS are used to indicate special areas or features, the nature of which can be seen by referring to a chart, Sailing Directions or Notices to Mariners. Such marks may be used, for example, to indicate a Traffic Separation Zone, a spoil ground, a military practice area, cable, pipeline or outfall pipes, a recreation zone reserved for, say, water skiers, and for automatic data acquisition buoys. They may be used also to mark, for example, the edges of a channel reserved for deep-draught vessels which is situated within a much wider channel marked by the usual red and green lateral buoys. In such a case the deep channel's sides are marked by the appropriate yellow conical or can buoys, or its centreline is marked by yellow spherical buoys.

Special Marks

Y   Y   Y   Y

These buoys are Yellow and may have a single yellow X top-mark. Buoy shape is optional, but should give a clear indication of the correct side to pass if this is important (e.g. an outfall buoy on the port side of the channel should be a yellow can). If lighted, a Yellow light is exhibited showing any rhythm that is different from the white lights of Cardinal, Isolated Danger and Safe Water marks, e.g. a Flashing yellow, or a Group Flashing yellow with 4 flashes might be used.

Chart symbols (below)

NEW DANGERS A rock, sandbank or wreck which is newly discovered and not yet shown on charts or in sailing directions, etc is called a New Danger. Such a danger is marked by one or more Cardinal or Lateral marks in accordance with the System A rules. If there is a grave risk to other vessels, at least one of the marks will be duplicated by an identical mark until the danger has been sufficiently notified to mariners in notices etc. If lighted, such a mark will exhibit a Quick or Very Quick Flashing light, white if it is a Cardinal mark, or red or green if it is a Lateral mark. The duplicate mark may carry a Racon, coded Morse D (— ··) to assist vessels with radar.

Marking of Secondary Channels
Yachts and other small vessels often find it necessary to navigate in narrow and shallow rivers and channels in order to reach their moorings or berths. Such channels are often maintained and marked by the local harbour authority and in some cases by local yacht clubs. The buoys and marks used do not always conform to the systems previously described.

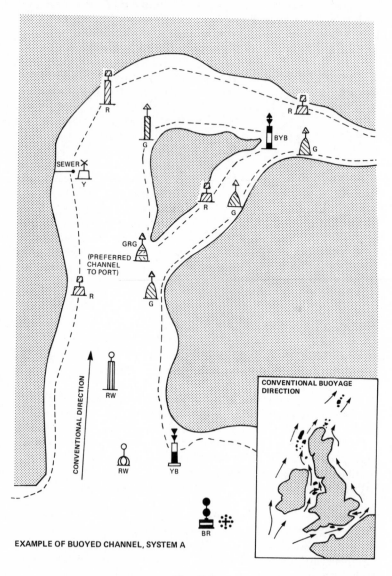

EXAMPLE OF BUOYED CHANNEL, SYSTEM A

Fig. 2.9

Port-hand buoys are usually can or barrel shaped, and starboard hand buoys usually conical, but other shapes are sometimes seen.

In some of the smaller rivers and harbours the edges of the channel are marked by pile beacons, perches or withies driven into the mud. Pile beacons are stout poles usually with some form of distinguishing topmark. Perches and withies are tree branches also sometimes fitted with topmarks. These are rarely fitted with lights for night navigation though they may have reflectors. Reference to a large scale chart or to the Pilot book for the area will usually show how to pass these marks in order to keep in the channel.

Port Traffic Signals

Agreement has been reached on standardised International Port Traffic Signals and it is expected that they will be introduced at ports as and when the need for change arises, starting (1983) with Dover and Shoreham. However, the installation of these signals will not be mandatory and they may not be used in every harbour where they might be suitable.

The new signals are lights only, shown by day and night. They are intended to control traffic movements in ports and port approaches, but may be used at locks and bridges as well.

Red Flashing lights indicate a serious emergency; otherwise lights will be Fixed or Slow Occulting to differentiate them from background glare.

1

ⓇⓇⓇ

Message
Serious emergency: all vessels stop or divert

Flashing

2

ⓇⓇⓇ

Message
Vessels not to proceed

3

ⒼⒼⒼ

Message
Proceed: one-way traffic

4

ⒼⒼⓌ

Message
Proceed: two-way traffic

5

ⒼⓌⒼ

Message
A vessel may proceed only when it has received specific orders to do so

Note Some ports may use an additional Yellow light, always to the left of the main top light, to allow small craft to disregard Messages 2 and 5.

2a Ⓨ Ⓡ
    Ⓡ
    Ⓡ

Vessels not to proceed, except that those which navigate outside main channel need not comply with main message.

5a Ⓨ Ⓖ
    Ⓦ
    Ⓖ

Vessel may proceed only when it has received specific orders to do so, except that vessels which navigate outside main channel need not comply with main message.

Chapter 3

Tides

Tides are the periodic vertical movements of sea level in response to the tide-generating forces of the moon and sun. The solar effect is only about three-sevenths of that of the moon because of the sun's greater distance from the earth. These tide-generating forces vary as the earth changes its position relative to the moon and sun during the course of each year, thus varying the tides produced. Modern tidal theory, however, suggests that the nature of the tides produced in response to the varying forces is mainly determined by the shapes, sizes and depths of the various oceans and seas, and also by the gyroscopic effect of the earth's rotation.

There are three more or less well defined types of tides, known as: Semi-diurnal tides, Diurnal tides and Mixed tides.

SEMI-DIURNAL TIDES are experienced on the coasts of the British Isles and Western Europe, and also in other parts of the world. At these ports sea level oscillates between high water (HW) and low water (LW), and there are two high waters and two low waters in each lunar day of about 24 hours 50 minutes. The height between successive high and low waters, called the RANGE of the tide, is only 2 metres at some ports that experience this type of tide, while other ports, which may be less than 100 miles away, experience tides with ranges of more than 10 metres. The semi-diurnal tides of the Gulf of St Malo, the Bristol Channel and the Bay of Fundy, with ranges exceeding 12 metres, have the greatest ranges of any tides experienced in the world.

The main characteristic of semi-diurnal tides is that the heights of successive high and low waters are very nearly the same for each day. Also the time interval between successive high and low waters, called the DURATION of the tide, is approximately a quarter of one lunar day, i.e. 6 hours 12 minutes.

The heights of successive high and successive low waters do change gradually as the moon changes phase. About $1\frac{1}{2}$ days after new moon and full moon, when the earth, moon and sun are nearly in line, the tides have the greatest range and the highest high waters and lowest low waters are experienced. These are known as SPRING tides, and they occur every 15 days throughout the year. The interval of $1\frac{1}{2}$ days between new moon and springs and full moon and springs is because the sea does not respond instantaneously to the lunar and solar tide-generating forces. Approximately $7\frac{1}{2}$ days after new moon and full moon, the lunar and solar tide forces are acting at right angles to each other, and about $1\frac{1}{2}$ days later tides of least range are produced, with lowest high waters and highest low waters. These are known as NEAP tides, and they also occur approximately every 15 days throughout the year, on each occasion just after the first and third quarters of the moon.

Between the days of spring tides and the next neap tides, the HW heights steadily decrease, while LW heights increase. Between the days of neap tides and the next spring tides, successive HW heights increase, while LW heights decrease.

DIURNAL TIDES Ports which experience this type of tide are situated mainly in or just out of the tropics. At these ports there is only one high water and one low water in each lunar day, and the range of tide produced is normally not large.

MIXED TIDES prevail on a large part of the Australian coast, on the Pacific coast of North America, and on the eastern shores of Asia and adjacent islands. There are two high waters and two low waters in each lunar day, but there is a marked inequality in the heights of successive high waters and successive low waters.

IMPORTANCE OF TIDES Vertical tidal movement is of no importance well offshore away from shoal areas, but in shallow rivers, port approaches and harbours the variation of a metre or so in sea level may make the difference between staying afloat and going aground. Certain berths and anchorages can only be reached at or about high water, and on these occasions it is important to know the approximate time of high water and to what height the tide will rise. It may on the other hand, be necessary to enter a port or cross a shoal patch at about low water, and again some knowledge of the height of tide at the time will assist in choosing a safe track, or deciding whether it is safe to enter. To assist the navigator in this respect, the Admiralty publish annually in the Admiralty Tide Tables (ATT) predictions of the times and heights of high and low water throughout the year at certain important ports. ATT are in three volumes:

Volume 1: European waters (including Mediterranean Sea)
Volume 2: The Atlantic and Indian Oceans
Volume 3: The Pacific Ocean and adjacent seas.

Each volume is divided into two parts as follows:

Part I – Tidal predictions for Standard Ports
Part II – Tidal data for Secondary Ports.

STANDARD PORTS are those ports for which the times and heights of high and low water have been predicted for every day of the year.

SECONDARY PORTS are those other ports or places for which sufficient tidal information is given in the Tables to enable the navigator to predict the times and heights of high and low water. This information is usually in the form of Time and Height Differences, which when applied to the predicted times and heights of a named Standard Port give the predicted times and heights at the Secondary Port.

All times are given for a certain meridian or zone, which is indicated on the page concerned. All heights are given in metres above CHART DATUM, except those preceded by minus signs which indicate the amount in metres that those tides are expected to fall below chart datum.

CHART DATUM is the zero level for all predictions in Admiralty Tide Tables. It is a level which is fixed for each port or place after a series of tidal observations have been made there, and is so low that the tide will rarely fall below it. It is the datum of soundings on the latest edition of the largest scale Admiralty chart of the place. On metric charts of the British Isles the datum at a place is established at the level of Lowest Astronomical Tide (LAT). When using fathoms charts with Admiralty Tide Tables a correction equal to the difference between LAT and the charted datum may have to be subtracted from predicted tide heights.

LAT is the lowest level which can be predicted to occur under average meteorological conditions and under any combination of astronomical conditions. Such a level will not be reached every year, and it should be noted that it is not the extreme level which can be reached, as storm surges may cause lower levels.

The following extracts from the ATT for European Waters will be used to show how the times of HW and LW can be obtained for a Standard Port and a Secondary Port. All times for British ports are

EXTRACTS FROM THE ADMIRALTY TIDE TABLES
VOL 1

(By permission of the Controller of H.M. Stationery Office and the Hydrographer of the Navy.)

CHANNEL ISLANDS - ST. HELIER

LAT 49°11'N   LONG 2°07'W

TIME ZONE GMT   TIMES AND HEIGHTS OF HIGH AND LOW WATERS

MAY

Day	TIME / m	Day	TIME / m
1 SU	0304 2.0 / 0842 10.0 / 1517 2.5 / 2056 9.9	16 M	0301 1.6 / 0834 10.6 / 1521 2.0 / 2051 10.6
2 M	0332 2.5 / 0912 9.5 / 1542 3.0 / 2128 9.3	17 TU	0343 2.1 / 0919 10.1 / 1604 2.5 / 2138 9.9
3 TU	0402 3.0 / 0948 8.8 / 1613 3.6 / 2206 8.7	18 W	0431 2.7 / 1012 9.4 / 1655 3.2 / 2235 9.2
4 W	0441 3.6 / 1031 8.2 / 1655 4.1 / 2259 8.1	19 TH	0530 3.2 / 1119 8.7 / 1803 3.7 / 2351 8.7
5 TH	0534 4.1 / 1142 7.6 / 1800 4.6	20 F	0648 3.6 / 1250 8.4 / 1928 3.9
6 F	0031 7.8 / 0655 4.4 / 1326 7.5 / 1937 4.7	21 SA	0123 8.6 / 0816 3.5 / 1416 8.7 / 2051 3.5
7 SA	0205 7.9 / 0826 4.2 / 1444 8.0 / 2105 4.2	22 SU	0240 9.0 / 0929 2.9 / 1521 9.3 / 2156 2.9
8 SU	0310 8.4 / 0938 3.7 / 1538 8.6 / 2204 3.6	23 M	0341 9.6 / 1028 2.4 / 1613 9.8 / 2249 2.3
9 M	0357 9.1 / 1028 3.0 / 1620 9.3 / 2251 2.9	24 TU	0431 10.1 / 1118 1.9 / 1659 10.3 / 2336 1.9
10 TU	0438 9.7 / 1112 2.4 / 1659 9.9 / 2333 2.3	25 W	0516 10.4 / 1203 1.7 / 1742 10.5
11 W	0516 10.2 / 1154 1.9 / 1736 10.5	26 TH	0019 1.7 / 0558 10.5 / 1243 1.6 / 1821 10.6
12 TH	0015 1.8 / 0556 10.7 / 1235 1.5 / 1814 10.9	27 F	0100 1.6 / 0639 10.5 / 1323 1.8 / 1857 10.5
13 F	0056 1.5 / 0634 11.0 / 1317 1.3 / 1852 11.2	28 SA	0138 1.7 / 0716 10.1 / 1357 2.0 / 1933 10.4
14 SA	0138 1.3 / 0713 11.1 / 1358 1.3 / 1931 11.2	29 SU	0213 1.9 / 0751 10.1 / 1427 2.3 / 2005 10.1
15 SU	0220 1.4 / 0754 11.0 / 1439 1.5 / 2011 11.0	30 M	0244 2.2 / 0825 9.7 / 1457 2.6 / 2039 9.8
		31 TU	0315 2.5 / 0858 9.4 / 1527 3.0 / 2112 9.5

JUNE

Day	TIME / m	Day	TIME / m
1	0349 2.9 / 0934 8.9 / 1559 3.4 / 2150 9.0	16	0433 2.1 / 1012 9.8 / 1655 2.7 / 2233 9.1
2	0426 3.3 / 1016 8.5 / 1638 3.8 / 2238 8.6	17	0526 2.7 / 1112 9.2 / 1753 3.2 / 2336 9.2
3	0512 3.7 / 1111 8.1 / 1730 4.2 / 2343 8.2	18	0631 3.1 / 1222 8.8 / 1902 3.6
4	0611 4.0 / 1222 7.9 / 1841 4.4	19	0048 8.9 / 0742 3.3 / 1337 8.7 / 2015 3.5
5	0059 8.1 / 0724 4.2 / 1338 8.0 / 2001 4.2	20	0201 8.9 / 0853 3.1 / 1443 8.9 / 2119 3.2
6	0208 8.3 / 0836 3.8 / 1439 8.5 / 2108 3.8	21	0305 9.1 / 0953 2.9 / 1541 9.2 / 2216 2.9
7	0303 8.6 / 0935 3.3 / 1529 9.1 / 2202 3.2	22	0400 9.4 / 1045 2.6 / 1630 9.6 / 2305 2.5
8	0352 9.3 / 1026 2.6 / 1616 9.8 / 2251 2.6	23	0451 9.6 / 1132 2.4 / 1715 9.8 / 2351 2.3
9	0438 9.9 / 1113 2.2 / 1701 10.3 / 2339 2.1	24	0537 9.8 / 1217 2.4 / 1757 10.0
10	0525 10.4 / 1203 1.8 / 1746 10.7	25	0035 2.2 / 0616 9.8 / 1257 2.3 / 1838 10.1
11	0029 1.7 / 0611 10.7 / 1253 1.5 / 1832 11.1	26	0117 2.1 / 0700 9.8 / 1335 2.4 / 1916 10.1
12	0120 1.4 / 0657 10.9 / 1342 1.4 / 1917 11.2	27	0155 2.1 / 0737 9.8 / 1411 2.4 / 1952 10.1
13	0209 1.3 / 0744 11.0 / 1430 1.4 / 2004 11.1	28	0230 2.2 / 0812 9.7 / 1443 2.5 / 2026 9.9
14	0257 1.3 / 0832 10.7 / 1517 1.7 / 2050 10.8	29	0304 2.3 / 0846 9.5 / 1514 2.7 / 2100 9.7
15	0345 1.7 / 0919 10.3 / 1604 2.2 / 2139 10.3	30	0336 2.5 / 0919 9.3 / 1546 3.0 / 2135 9.4

JULY

Day	TIME / m	Day	TIME / m
1 F	0410 2.9 / 0955 9.0 / 1621 3.3 / 2213 9.1	16 SA	0509 2.1 / 1047 9.7 / 1729 2.7 / 2306 9.6
2 SA	0447 3.2 / 1035 8.7 / 1701 3.7 / 2257 8.7	17 SU	0558 2.8 / 1142 9.1 / 1822 3.3
3 SU	0530 3.6 / 1125 8.4 / 1750 3.9 / 2351 8.4	18 M	0004 9.0 / 0657 3.3 / 1245 8.6 / 1927 3.6
4 M	0624 3.8 / 1224 8.3 / 1853 4.1	19 TU	0112 8.6 / 0805 3.6 / 1357 8.4 / 2034 3.7
5 TU	0056 8.3 / 0730 3.8 / 1333 8.4 / 2005 3.9	20 W	0225 8.5 / 0912 3.6 / 1504 8.5 / 2138 3.5
6 W	0204 8.5 / 0837 3.6 / 1437 8.8 / 2111 3.5	21 TH	0331 8.6 / 1012 3.4 / 1603 8.8 / 2235 3.2
7 TH	0307 8.9 / 0941 3.1 / 1538 9.3 / 2212 3.0	22 F	0430 8.8 / 1105 3.2 / 1654 9.2 / 2327 2.9
8 F	0407 9.4 / 1040 2.6 / 1634 9.9 / 2311 2.4	23 SA	0549 9.1 / 1153 2.9 / 1740 9.5
9 SA	0504 10.0 / 1132 9.4 / 1727 10.5	24 SU	0015 2.6 / 0605 9.4 / 1236 2.7 / 1822 9.8
10 SU	0010 1.9 / 0557 10.5 / 1236 1.7 / 1819 11.0	25 M	0100 2.3 / 0646 9.7 / 1317 2.5 / 1902 10.1
11 M	0107 1.4 / 0649 10.9 / 1331 1.9 / 1909 11.3	26 TU	0140 2.1 / 0723 9.8 / 1354 2.3 / 1937 10.2
12 TU	0201 1.0 / 0738 11.4 / 1422 1.2 / 1957 11.4	27 W	0216 2.0 / 0757 9.9 / 1427 2.2 / 2011 10.3
13 W	0250 0.9 / 0826 11.1 / 1510 1.2 / 2043 11.2	28 TH	0249 2.0 / 0827 9.9 / 1500 2.3 / 2042 10.2
14 TH	0338 1.1 / 0912 10.8 / 1556 1.6 / 2129 10.8	29 F	0319 2.1 / 0857 9.9 / 1529 2.5 / 2111 10.0
15 F	0423 1.5 / 0959 10.3 / 1641 2.1 / 2216 10.2	30 SA	0349 2.4 / 0927 9.6 / 1557 2.8 / 2142 9.7
		31 SU	0419 2.7 / 0959 9.3 / 1628 3.1 / 2216 9.3

AUGUST

Day	TIME / m	Day	TIME / m
1 M	0449 3.1 / 1037 9.0 / 1704 3.5 / 2258 8.9	16 TU	0605 3.5 / 1149 8.5 / 1831 3.8
2 TU	0530 3.5 / 1123 8.7 / 1754 3.8 / 2351 8.5	17 W	0015 8.3 / 0706 4.1 / 1300 8.0 / 1940 4.2
3 W	0628 3.8 / 1228 8.4 / 1904 4.0	18 TH	0138 7.9 / 0823 4.3 / 1427 7.9 / 2058 4.1
4 TH	0106 8.3 / 0745 3.8 / 1348 8.5 / 2027 3.8	19 F	0305 7.9 / 0939 4.2 / 1541 8.3 / 2210 3.8
5 F	0230 8.5 / 0905 3.5 / 1508 8.9 / 2145 3.3	20 SA	0414 8.3 / 1042 3.8 / 1637 8.8 / 2308 3.3
6 SA	0348 9.1 / 1019 3.0 / 1617 9.6 / 2254 2.6	21 SU	0506 8.9 / 1133 3.3 / 1723 9.4 / 2357 2.7
7 SU	0451 9.8 / 1125 2.3 / 1716 10.4 / 2358 1.9	22 M	0549 9.4 / 1217 2.8 / 1804 9.9
8 M	0549 10.6 / 1225 1.6 / 1810 11.1	23 TU	0041 2.3 / 0627 9.8 / 1256 2.3 / 1841 10.3
9 TU	0057 1.2 / 0641 11.2 / 1320 1.1 / 1859 11.6	24 W	0119 1.9 / 0702 10.1 / 1333 2.0 / 1916 10.5
10 W	0149 0.7 / 0728 11.5 / 1411 0.8 / 1945 11.8	25 TH	0154 1.7 / 0733 10.3 / 1406 1.9 / 1947 10.6
11 TH	0237 0.4 / 0812 11.6 / 1456 0.8 / 2029 11.7	26 F	0226 1.6 / 0801 10.4 / 1437 1.9 / 2015 10.6
12 F	0321 0.6 / 0854 11.3 / 1538 1.1 / 2110 11.3	27 SA	0256 1.7 / 0829 10.4 / 1505 2.0 / 2043 10.4
13 SA	0402 1.1 / 0934 10.7 / 1617 1.7 / 2149 10.6	28 SU	0322 2.0 / 0856 10.2 / 1532 2.4 / 2110 10.1
14 SU	0441 1.9 / 1014 10.0 / 1655 2.4 / 2231 9.8	29 M	0349 2.4 / 0925 9.9 / 1557 2.8 / 2141 9.8
15 M	0520 2.7 / 1057 9.2 / 1737 3.2 / 2316 9.0	30 TU	0414 2.9 / 0957 9.5 / 1627 3.2 / 2217 9.3
		31 W	0449 3.4 / 1040 9.0 / 1711 3.7 / 2306 8.7

Table 3.1

FRANCE, NORTH COAST; CHANNEL ISLANDS   333

No.	PLACE	Lat. N.	Long. E.	TIME DIFFERENCES High Water (Zone −0100)		Low Water		HEIGHT DIFFERENCES (IN METRES) MHWS	MHWN	MLWN	MLWS	M.L. Z₀ m.	
1605	ST. HELIER .	(see page 210)		0300 and 1500	0900 and 2100	0200 and 1400	0900 and 2100	11·1	8·1	4·1	1·3		
	Channel Islands			(Zone G.M.T.)									
	Alderney												
1603	Braye .	49 43	2 12	+0040	+0050	+0025	+0105	−4·8	−3·4	−1·5	−0·5	3·62	
	Sark												
1603a	Maseline Pier .	49 26	2 21	+0015	+0005	+0005	+0010	−2·1	−1·5	−0·6	−0·3	4·87	
	Guernsey												
1604	St. Peter Port .	49 27	2 31	+0012	0000	−0008	+0002	−2·1	−1·4	−0·6	−0·3	5·04	
	Jersey												
1605	**ST. HELIER** .	49 11	2 07	STANDARD PORT				See Table V				6·06	
1606	St. Catherine Bay .	49 13	2 01	0000	+0010	+0010	+0010	0·0	−0·1	0·0	+0·1	6·0	x
1607	Les Ecrehou .	49 17	1 56	+0004	+0012	+0010	+0020	−0·2	+0·3	−0·3	0·0	6·15	
1608	Les Minquiers .	48 58	2 08	+0007	0000	−0008	+0013	+0·4	+0·9	−0·1	+0·1	6·47	

Table 3.1a

given in Greenwich Mean Time (GMT) so that during British Summer Time (BST) one hour must be added to the predicted times for these ports.

All other times are given in the Standard Time for the place concerned which is stated on the page for that port.

Example. What is the afternoon time and height of LW at Braye (Alderney) on 16 May, and the time and height of the following HW?

The general index at the back of the Tide Tables shows a number (1603) against Braye. This indicates that it is a Secondary Port, and that the information for Braye will be found against No. 1603 in Part II of the Tables. Standard Ports are printed in the Index in capitals, with the page numbers and place reference number, e.g. ST HELIER (predictions p. 210–13) ... 1605.

On turning to No. 1603 in Part II (see Table 3.1a) it will be seen that St Helier is the Standard Port, and that predictions for St Helier are given on page 210, which is the first of 4 pages of information. On turning to the page for May the predictions are seen displayed as in Table 3.1. These times are for GMT and are as follows for PM on 16 May:

ST HELIER

LW   1521   2·0 m   HW   2051   10·6 m

On returning to the page for Braye (1603), it will be seen that time differences are related to specific times of HW and LW at St Helier, and that the height differences are related to specific heights of HW and LW.

The Table predicts that if LW at St Helier is at 0200 or 1400, the time difference for LW at Braye is +25 minutes, but if it is at 0900 or 2100, then the time difference is +1 hour 5 minutes. If LW at St Helier on the day in question comes between the times quoted, it is necessary to adjust the time difference by interpolation. LW on the day in the example is at 1521 which comes between 1400 and 2100 and the working might be laid out as:

Time for day		1521	Change from 1400 = 81 mins
Reference times	1400 ↗	2100	Change 420 mins
Time differences	+0025 →?	+0105	Change 40 mins

The correction to +0025 is in proportion to the change between 1400 and 1521, and 1400 and 2100, and is therefore 81/420 × 40 minutes equal to 8 minutes, which makes the time difference on the day equal to +0025 + 8 = 33 minutes.

Similarly, if HW St Helier on the day comes between the reference times, interpolation is necessary. In this example HW St Helier is at 2051, which is near enough to the reference time of 2100 to use the time difference given for that time, i.e. +50 minutes. The time differences to apply in this example are therefore +33 minutes for LW and +50 minutes for HW.

Height differences have to be adjusted using the same method if the heights predicted for St Helier on the day in the example differ from the reference heights shown in Part II. In this example the position is as under for LW:

Height for day		2·0m	Change from 1·3 = 0·7m
Reference Hts	4·1m	1·3m	Change 2·8m
Ht differences	−1·5m	? ← −0·5m	Change 1·0m

The correction to −0·5m is in proportion to the change between 1·3 and 2·0, and 1·3 and 4·1, and is therefore 0·7/2·8 × 1·0m which equals −0·25m. The corrected height difference is −0·5m plus −0·25m giving −0·75 or −0·8m approx.

By the same reasoning and method, the correction to apply to the −3·4m height difference is 2·5/3·0 × 1·4m equal to −1·2m giving −4·6m as the HW height difference.

The predicted times and heights for Braye are therefore:

St Helier	GMT LW	1521	2·0m	HW	2051	10·6m
Differences		+0033	−0·8m		+0050	−4·6m
Braye	GMT LW	1554	1·2m	HW	2141	6·0m

In practice, if the predicted quantities are set down on paper as shown above, it is usually possible to estimate time and height differences by eye with sufficient accuracy for practical purposes.

The four heights given against St Helier in Part II, i.e. 11·1m, 8·1m, 4·1m and 1·3m are the heights of four specific tidal levels at St Helier. These are MEAN HIGH WATER SPRIN 3S (MHWS)   11·1m
          and MEAN LOW WATER SPRINGS (MLWS)   1·3m
which are the average values of two successive high waters and two successive low waters at those periods of 24 hours (approximately once a fortnight), when the range of tide is greatest and calculated over a year when the moon's average maximum declination is $23\frac{1}{2}°$.

          MEAN HIGH WATER NEAPS   (MHWN)   8·1m
and MEAN LOW WATER NEAPS   (MLWN)   4·1m
are average values calculated for similar conditions but when the range of tide is least.

The heights of these tidal levels are given for all Standard Ports in Table V at the front of the ATT and in Part II as previously shown. The heights of similar levels at Secondary Ports are obtained by applying the height differences in Part II to the Standard Port heights as appropriate, e.g.

Braye MHWS: $11·1 - 4·8 = 6·3$m
      MHWN: $8·1 - 3·4 = 4·7$m
      MLWN: $4·1 - 1·5 = 2·6$m
      MLWS: $1·3 - 0·5 = 0·8$m

The heights of MHWS, MHWN, MLWN and MLWS for selected places are also printed in Tables and displayed on large scale charts. These Tables also give information enabling the datum at a place to be fixed with respect to Ordnance Datum (Newlyn), the reference level of the land levelling system of the British Isles (Table 3.2).

The information contained in such a table is often useful if Tide Tables are not available for making an approximate estimate of the

Tidal Levels referred to Datum of Soundings

| | Lat. | Long. | Heights in metres above datum | | | | |
Place	N	W	MHWS	MHWN	MLWN	MLWS	Datum and remarks
Sennen Cove	50° 04′	5° 42′	6·1	4·8	—	—	
Penzance	50 06	5 33	5·6	4·4	2·0	0·8	3·05m below Ordnance Datum (Newlyn)
Porthleven	50 05	5 19	5·5	4·3	2·0	0·8	2·99m below Ordnance Datum (Newlyn)
Lizard Point	49 57	5 12	5·3	4·2	1·9	0·6	2·90m below Ordnance Datum (Newlyn)
Coverack	50 01	5 05	5·3	4·2	1·9	0·6	2·90m below Ordnance Datum (Newlyn)
Helford R Entrance	50 05	5 05	5·3	4·2	1·9	0·6	2·90m below Ordnance Datum (Newlyn)
Falmouth	50 09	5 03	5·3	4·2	1·9	0·6	2·91m below Ordnance Datum (Newlyn)

Reproduced from British Admiralty Chart No. 777 with the permission of the Controller of H.M. Stationery Office and of the Hydrographer of the Navy

Table 3.2

least depth of water available at about LW, or the maximum available at about HW.

Tidal predictions for the British Isles and Western Europe from the Bay of Biscay to North West Germany are also contained in Reed's Nautical Almanac, but in an abbreviated form. The predicted heights and times of HW and LW are given for all Standard Ports, and the mean HW and LW Time and Height Differences referred to selected Standard Ports are given for each Secondary Port to enable the approximate times and heights of HW and LW there to be obtained (Tables 3.3 and 3.3a).

ST. HELIER, JERSEY CHANNEL ISLANDS

HIGH & LOW WATER

G.M.T. ADD 1 HOUR FOR B.S.T.

	MAY				JUNE				JULY				AUGUST		
Time h.min.	Ht. m.	Time h.min.	Ht. m.	Time h.min.	Ht. m.	Time h.min.	Ht. m.	Time h.min.	Ht. m.	Time h.min.	Ht. m.	Time h.min.	Ht. m.	Time h.min.	Ht. m.
1 0304	2.0	**16** 0301	1.6	**1** 0349	2.9	**16** 0433	2.1	**1** 0410	2.9	**16** 0509	2.1	**1** 0449	3.1	**16** 0605	3.5
0842	10.0	0834	10.6	0934	8.9	1012	9.8	0955	9.0	1047	9.7	1037	9.0	1149	8.5
Su 1517	2.5	M 1521	1.9	W 1559	3.4	Th 1655	2.7	F 1621	3.3	Sa 1729	2.7	M 1704	3.5	Tu 1831	3.8
2056	9.9	2051	10.6	2150	9.0	2233	9.7	2213	9.1	2306	9.6	2258	8.9	—	—
2 0332	2.5	**17** 0343	2.1	**2** 0426	3.3	**17** 0526	2.7	**2** 0447	3.2	**17** 0558	2.8	**2** 0530	3.5	**17** 0015	8.3
0912	9.4	0919	10.1	1016	8.5	1112	9.2	1035	8.7	1142	9.1	1123	8.7	0706	4.1
M 1542	3.0	Tu 1604	2.5	Th 1638	3.8	F 1753	3.2	Sa 1701	3.6	Su 1822	3.3	Tu 1754	3.8	W 1300	8.0
2128	9.3	2138	9.9	2238	8.5	2336	9.2	2257	8.7	—	—	2351	8.5	1940	4.2
3 0402	3.0	**18** 0431	2.7	**3** 0512	3.7	**18** 0631	3.1	**3** 0530	3.6	**18** 0004	9.0	**3** 0628	3.8	**18** 0138	7.9
0948	8.8	1012	9.4	1111	8.1	1222	8.8	1125	8.4	0657	3.3	1228	8.4	0823	4.3
Tu 1613	3.6	W 1655	3.2	F 1730	4.2	Sa 1902	3.5	Su 1750	3.9	M 1245	8.6	W 1904	4.0	Th 1427	7.9
2206	8.7	2235	9.2	2343	8.2	—	—	2351	8.4	1927	3.6	—	—	2058	4.1
4 0441	3.6	**19** 0530	3.2	**4** 0611	4.0	**19** 0048	8.9	**4** 0624	3.8	**19** 0112	8.6	**4** 0106	8.3	**19** 0305	7.9
1031	8.2	1119	8.7	1222	7.9	0742	3.3	1224	8.3	0805	3.6	0745	3.8	0939	4.2
W 1655	4.1	Th 1803	3.7	Sa 1841	4.4	Su 1337	8.7	M 1853	4.0	Tu 1357	8.4	Th 1348	8.5	F 1541	8.3
2259	8.1	2351	8.7	—	—	2015	3.5	—	—	2034	3.7	2027	3.8	2210	3.8
5 0534	4.1	**20** 0648	3.6	**5** 0059	8.1	**20** 0201	8.9	**5** 0056	8.3	**20** 0225	8.5	**5** 0230	8.5	**20** 0414	8.3
1142	7.6	1250	8.4	0724	4.1	0853	3.1	0730	3.8	0912	3.6	0905	3.5	1042	3.7
Th 1800	4.6	F 1928	3.9	Su 1338	8.0	M 1443	8.9	Tu 1333	8.4	W 1504	8.5	F 1508	8.9	Sa 1637	8.8
—	—	—	—	2001	4.2	2119	3.2	2005	3.9	2138	3.5	2145	3.3	2308	3.3
6 0031	7.7	**21** 0123	8.6	**6** 0208	8.3	**21** 0305	9.1	**6** 0204	8.5	**21** 0331	8.6	**6** 0348	9.1	**21** 0506	8.8
0655	4.4	0816	3.5	0836	3.8	0953	2.9	0837	3.6	1012	3.4	1019	3.0	1133	3.3
F 1326	7.5	Sa 1416	8.7	M 1439	8.5	Tu 1541	9.2	W 1437	8.8	Th 1603	8.8	Sa 1637	9.6	Su 1723	9.4
1937	4.7	2051	3.5	2108	3.7	2216	2.9	2111	3.5	2235	3.2	2254	2.6	2357	2.7
7 0205	7.9	**22** 0240	9.0	**7** 0303	8.8	**22** 0400	9.4	**7** 0307	8.9	**22** 0430	8.8	**7** 0451	9.8	**22** 0549	9.4
0826	4.2	0929	2.9	0935	3.3	1045	2.6	0941	3.1	1105	3.2	1125	2.3	1217	2.8
Sa 1444	8.0	Su 1521	9.3	Tu 1529	9.1	W 1630	9.5	Th 1538	9.3	F 1654	9.2	Su 1716	10.4	M 1804	9.9
2105	4.2	2156	2.9	2202	3.2	2305	2.5	2212	3.0	2327	2.9	2358	1.9	—	—

Table 3.3

The previous example to find the times and heights of the afternoon low water and the following high water at Alderney (Braye) on 16 May is now worked out using the extracts from Reed's Nautical Almanac.

The page number for Alderney (Braye) is obtained from the Tidal Index at the back of the Almanac. The standard port for Braye is again St Helier and by inspection of the extracts the following information is obtained:

TIDAL DIFFERENCES ON ST. HELIER

PLACE	MHW		MLW		RULING DEPTH AT			
	Tm. Diff.	Ht. Diff.	Tm. Diff.	Ht. Diff.	HWS	HWN	CD	
	h. min.	m.	h. min.	m.	m.	m.	m.	POSITION
Channel Islands								
The Casquets ...	+0 22	—	—	—	—	—	27.4	Anchorage S.E.
Alderney (Braye)	+0 45	−4.8S −3.4N	+0 45	−1.0	15.4	13.8	9.1	Anchorage off
Guernsey								
St. Peter Port ...	+0 05	−1.7	−0 05	−0.4	10.8 18.8	8.5 16.5	1.8 9.8	Grand Havre (Anche.) Anchorage off
Jersey								
St. Helier	0 00	0.0	0 00	0.0	13.8	10.8	2.7.	Entce. and S. part new Harbour
Rozel	−0 09	−0.1	—	0.0	—	—	Dries	Harbour
Gorey	−0 05	—			16.9	15.4	9.1	Outer Road. Harb. dries
Les Ecrehoux ...	+0 10	0.0	+0 15	−0.1	13.9	11.4	3.0	Anch. close Marmotier
Les Minquiers ..	+0 05	+0.6	0 00	0.0	—	—	—	
Iles Chausey	−0 15	+1.7	0 00	+0.7	—	—	—	

Reproduced from *Reed's Nautical Almanac* by kind permission of Thos. Reed Publications

Table 3.3a

St Helier	GMT LW	1521	1·9m	HW	2051	10·6m
Differences		+ 045	−1·0m		+ 045	−4·6m*
Braye	GMT LW	1606	0·9m	HW	2136	6·0m

* The height difference for HW is obtained by interpolating between −4·8 S and −3·4 N given in the table. This is achieved using the 'Guiding Depths' for St Helier lower down the page. By subtracting Chart Datum (CD) 2·7m from HWS 13·8m and HWN 10·8m, the Spring height 11·1m and Neap height 8·1m are obtained. These are then compared as with the Admiralty tables as follows:

Height for day		10·6m change from	11·1m = 0·5m
Reference Heights (S)	11·1m	(N)	8·1m change 3·0m
Ht differences	−4·8m ⟶ ?		−3·4m change 1·4m

The correction to −4·8m is 0·5/3·0 × 1·4m which equals 0·2m making the height difference for the day −4·6m.

For a boat keeping British Summer Time, one hour should be added to the above times.

SHALLOW WATER EFFECTS On the English coast between Portland and Selsey Bill, on certain parts of the Netherlands coast, in the Bay of the Seine, and in most rivers and estuaries, the normal tidal pattern of semi-diurnal tides is distorted by what are known as 'shallow water effects'. At some ports in these areas, shallow water effects cause two high waters in succession followed by a normal low water, or two low waters in succession followed by a normal high water. These tides have what are known as double high waters or double low waters. At other ports in the same areas the tide remains at the same level for an appreciable time at high water, or at low water, and a 'stand' of the tide is said to occur.

The Tide Tables predict the times and heights of both high waters or both low waters at ports where double tides occur, and also indicate at which ports there is a stand of the tide and when it occurs.

HEIGHT OF TIDE AT ANY TIME BETWEEN HIGH AND LOW WATER The rate of rise and fall of any tide will not be uniform. Generally, at places where the tide is not distorted by shallow water effects, the rate of rise and fall is least near high and low water, and greatest near half tide or mean level.

In the Admiralty Tide Tables individual spring and neap curves are provided for each Standard Port (Fig. 3.1). To obtain the height of tide at a given time, this time is compared with the time of HW to obtain the 'Interval from high water' in hours and minutes, negative for times before HW and positive for those after. The Interval is entered against the spring curve for tides having approximately the spring range or greater, to obtain the Factor. For tides having approximately the neap range or less, the Interval is entered against the neap curve to read off the Factor. When the range of tide on the day puts it between springs and neaps, both curves are used and if necessary the resulting Factor is obtained by interpolation between the spring and neap answers. The Factor multiplied by the Range of the tide in question gives the Rise of tide which added to LW height predicts the required height of tide.

Example Determine the height of tide at Devonport at 0400 GMT (0500 BST) on 16 May.

Fig. 3.1

From predictions for Devonport on 16 May:

HW 0810 GMT 5·2m	HW 0810 GMT	Rise = 0·35 ×
		4·4 = 1·5m
LW 0155 GMT 0·8m	Given 0400 GMT	LW height = 0·8m
Range 4·4m	*Interval* −0410	*Ht of tide* = 2·3m
Factor from Spring curve = 0·35		

The range on the day (4·4m) is close to the Spring range (4·7m), so the graph has been entered at the top with −0410 and where this line meets the curve gives 0·35 as the Factor at the left-hand side. The Factor multiplied by the Range for the day gives the Rise which added to the LW height produces the required predicted Height of tide above Chart Datum.

The procedure can be reversed to calculate the time when the tide reaches a certain height. The required height is compared with LW height to give the Rise. The Rise divided by Range produces the Factor, which is then entered against the appropriate curve to give the Interval, negative to HW time for a rising tide, or positive for a falling tide. The Interval applied to the HW time predicts the time required.

The above method can be used to calculate intermediate heights at a secondary port using the Standard Port curves, if it is assumed that the tide at the secondary port rises and falls in a similar way. Results should be used with caution.

A Rise of Tide graph and standard curves with full instructions for use are given in Reed's Nautical Almanac, to enable intermediate heights to be calculated.

There are considerable shallow water effects on the tide at places between Swanage and Selsey, and special low water curves are provided in the ATT for such places and in Reed's Almanac for Poole.

There is important information in the Introduction to the Admiralty Tide Tables about the effects of varying meteorological conditions, barometric pressure, etc on tides and tidal streams, particularly in the southern North Sea. It is always worth reading this section before using the Tables for the first time.

It may not always be convenient to use the above-mentioned tables. The following approximate **Rule of Twelfths** may be used instead to estimate, with sufficient accuracy for most practical purposes, the height of tide at specific intervals from HW or LW at places where there are no shallow water effects. There are no simple rules that can be used instead of the curves for the Solent area, however.

The duration and range of the tide concerned should first be obtained from the Tide Tables. The duration should then be divided by six, and the range by twelve. Working from either HW or LW, a tide may be expected to rise or fall approximately:

1/12th	of its range in the first sixth of its duration;
2/12ths	,,	,,	,,	second sixth ,,	,,
3/12ths	,,	,,	,,	third sixth	,,	,,
3/12ths	,,	,,	,,	fourth sixth	,,	,,
2/12ths	,,	,,	,,	fifth sixth	,,	,,
1/12th	,,	,,	,,	last sixth	,,	,,

Thus using the information given above for Devonport for 16 May:

HW	0810 GMT	5·2m	1/12th range	0·4m
LW	0155 GMT	0·8m	2/12ths range	0·7m
Duration 0615		*Range* 4·4m	3/12ths range	1·1m
1/6th of Duration ... 0102½			

Approximate times and heights as the tide rises are predicted as:

LW	0155	0·8m	at	0502	3·0m
1st sixth	+0102	+0·4m	4th sixth	+0103	+1·1m
at	0257	1·2m	at	0605	4·1m
2nd sixth	+0103	+0·7m	5th sixth	+0102	+0·7m
at	0400	1·9m	at	0707	4·8m
3rd sixth	+0102	+1·1m	6th sixth	+0103	+0·4m
at	0502	3·0m	at	0810	5·2m

Heights at shorter intervals can be obtained by graphing the above quantities, heights against times, and then lifting off heights at the required times by inspection. Such information should be used with caution.

CHARTED DEPTHS OR SOUNDINGS The figures marked on that part of a chart which represents the sea indicate depths of water, known as soundings, in metres, or fathoms and feet, below Chart Datum. The unit used is always stated on each chart below its title. On metric charts it is shown in addition outside the chart border in magenta. The centre of the space occupied by a sounding represents the position of the depth indicated. On metric charts generally soundings are shown in metres and decimetres in depths of 21 metres or less, and to nearest half metre or in metres elsewhere.

e.g. 6_9 represents a depth of 6 metres 9 decimetres (6·9m)

0_7 represents a depth of 0 metres 7 decimetres (0·7m).

On fathoms charts generally soundings are shown in fathoms and feet in depths of less than 11 fathoms and in fathoms elsewhere. Some older charts show soundings in fathoms and fractions of a fathom,

e.g. 7_5 represents a depth of 7 fathoms 5 feet

0_2 represents a depth of 0 fathoms 2 feet

$6\frac{3}{4}$ represents a depth of 6 fathoms $4\frac{1}{2}$ feet.

There will not be usually *less* water than the charted soundings because the tide rarely falls below Chart Datum. On the few occasions at springs when the tide does fall below Chart Datum at some places, there will be less than the charted soundings for short periods at low water.

The underlined figures, e.g. $\underline{0_9}$ or $\underline{8}$, marked on banks and rocks which uncover, express the height in metres and decimetres, on metric charts, or in feet on fathoms charts, respectively, that the bank or rock dries when the tide falls to Chart Datum.

To estimate the depth of water at any time and place, it is

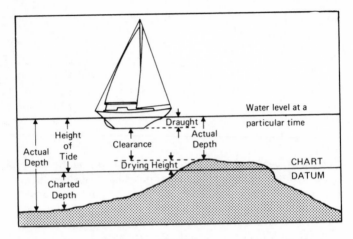

Fig. 3.2

only necessary to add the charted depth to the height of the tide or, in the case of a bank that dries, to subtract the drying height from the predicted height of tide. This is clearly shown in Fig. 3.2.

DEPTH CONTOURS On most charts appropriate distinguishing lines are drawn to enclose areas which have a certain depth or less, in a similar manner to the contour lines drawn on Ordnance Survey or other topographical maps.

To emphasise the shallow water areas on many charts, a blue tint is between the HW line and the 5m line (or 3 fathoms on fathoms charts), and a ribbon of blue tint on the shoal side of the 10m line (or 6 fathoms on fathoms charts). Sometimes other contour lines may be tinted. On metric charts areas which dry are green.

QUALITY OF THE BOTTOM The nature of the sea bed is indicated by the abbreviations shown in the following table. This information may be important when looking for an anchorage with good holding ground, but too much trust should not be placed on the charted information as the sample was probably obtained by means of a lead armed with tallow which only gives an indication of the surface material. Some chart abbreviations are:

Gd	Ground	Oy	Oysters	S	Sand	M	Mud
Oz	Ooze	Bo	Boulders	Cy	Clay	G	Gravel
Sn	Shingle	P	Pebbles	St	Stones	R	Rock

Ck	Chalk	Ms	Mussels	Sh	Shells	Cn	Cinders
Wd	Weed	f	Fine	c	Coarse	so	Soft

TIDAL STREAMS (sometimes called tidal currents) are the periodical *horizontal* movements of the sea in response to the tide-generating forces of the moon and sun. Tidal streams react to changes in these forces, as do the tides, so that the direction and/or speed of movement of the water vary continuously throughout each lunar day and month. A tidal stream is described by stating the direction *towards* which the water is moving, and by giving the speed (rate) of movement of the water in knots. For example, a northerly stream with a rate of 2 knots means that the water is moving towards north (is north-going) at a speed of 2 knots.

In a tidal river the stream is often closely related to the rise and fall of the tide there. When the tide is rising, the stream flows into the river until at or near HW it slackens, turns, and then flows in the reverse direction as the tide falls, until it slackens again at LW. The period when there is little or no stream is known as slack water. Nevertheless, slack water does not necessarily coincide with the times of high and low water. In rivers the stream is usually strongest in mid-stream in the straight reaches, but is usually stronger on the outside of bends. It usually pays therefore when making headway against the stream to keep near the bank in straight reaches, and on the inside of bends to avoid the main strength of the flow, bearing in mind that there will probably be less water available there than in midstream.

In wide channels such as the English Channel, tidal streams generally follow the trend of the channel for about 6 hours in each direction, except close to the coast where they may follow the trend of the coastline and cause indraughts into large bays and inlets. A clear indication of the set or direction of the stream is given by ships at anchor riding head-on to it, or by buoys canting away from it, or by the ripple of water in the wake of buoys, piles and other fixed objects. This indication is of great assistance when berthing, anchoring or mooring, and it can save much time and labour when using the dinghy between yacht and shore.

TIDAL STREAM PREDICTIONS for specified positions are arranged in tables on most charts of coastal waters and are shown by means of arrows on the small charts contained in Admiralty Pocket Tidal Stream Atlases and Nautical Almanacs. Tidal streams are also described in each 'Pilot'. The information given is always referred to the time of HW at a Standard Port. On charts and in the Tidal Stream

Atlases predicted directions and rates are given hourly commencing with predictions for a time which is 6 hours before HW at the Standard Port, and ending with predictions for a time which is 6 hours after HW at the Standard Port. The rates shown against each predicted direction are the Mean Spring rate which occurs on days when Spring Tides (maximum range) are experienced, and the mean Neap rate which occurs on days when Neap tides (minimum range) are experienced.

How to use the Predictions
1. TABLES PRINTED ON CHARTS
Some of the tables on BA Chart 1828 – England SE Coast, Dover to N. Foreland are shown in Tables 3.4 and 3.6.

Tidal Streams referred to HW at DOVER

	51°15'2N 1 32·6E (A)			51°13'3N 1 26·6E (H)			51°13'0N 1 36·4E (K)			51°10'5N 1 32·2E (L)			51°09'0N 1 27·8E (M)			51°06'6N 1 33·3E (N)			51°06'6N 1 20·4E (P)			
		Rate(kn)			Rate(kn)			Rate(kn)			Rate(kn)			Rate(kn)			Rate(kn)			Rate(kn)		
Hours	Dir	Sp	Np	Dir	Sp	Np	Dir	Sp	Np	Dir	Sp	Np	Dir	Sp	Np	Dir	Sp	Np	Dir	Sp	Np	Hours
Before HW 6	223	1·9	1·1	181	1·6	0·9	190	0·9	0·5	225	1·7	1·0	212	2·2	1·2	219	1·1	0·6	224	2·3	1·3	6 Before HW
5	228	2·5	1·4	183	2·1	1·1	191	2·3	1·3	225	2·5	1·4	213	2·2	1·2	227	2·5	1·4	231	2·5	1·4	5
4	226	3·1	1·7	186	2·1	1·2	195	3·1	1·7	222	3·1	1·7	216	1·9	1·1	225	3·6	2·0	233	2·4	1·3	4
3	225	3·1	1·7	188	1·9	1·0	196	3·2	1·8	219	2·9	1·6	228	1·3	0·8	224	3·2	1·8	225	1·5	0·8	3
2	231	1·2	0·7	190	0·8	0·5	195	2·0	1·1	224	1·4	0·8		Slack		220	1·8	1·0	075	0·3	0·2	2
1	040	1·3	0·7	007	0·9	0·5		Slack		014	0·5	0·3	032	1·2	0·7	050	0·4	0·2	056	2·3	1·3	1
HW	041	2·7	1·5	001	2·1	1·2	013	1·3	0·7	040	2·2	1·2	038	2·0	1·2	043	2·1	1·2	063	3·9	2·2	HW
After HW 1	043	2·8	1·6	001	2·3	1·3	015	2·4	1·4	042	3·0	1·7	039	2·3	1·3	046	3·0	1·6	064	4·1	2·3	1 After HW
2	046	2·5	1·4	003	2·3	1·3	014	3·1	1·7	037	2·8	1·6	034	2·2	1·2	044	3·2	1·8	066	3·5	1·9	2
3	049	1·7	1·0	002	1·4	0·8	017	2·6	1·5	047	1·9	1·1	031	1·5	0·8	040	2·4	1·3	072	2·6	1·4	3
4	055	0·7	0·4	017	0·6	0·3	018	1·7	1·0	061	0·9	0·5		Slack		038	0·9	0·5	087	1·3	0·7	4
5	171	0·2	0·1	161	0·3	0·2	018	0·6	0·3	167	0·3	0·2	203	1·0	0·6		Slack		208	1·1	0·6	5
6	219	1·5	0·9	180	1·3	0·7	189	0·5	0·3	218	1·3	0·7	210	1·8	1·0	210	0·8	0·4	220	2·2	1·2	6

Table 3.4

Each table shows the predicted tidal streams at the position given. Each position is identified on the chart by marking it with the appropriate lettered diamond ⟨A⟩ or ⟨H⟩ or ⟨M⟩ etc., which is also marked at the head of the column to which it refers. The left hand column shows that the Standard Port is Dover, and shows the hours before and after HW at Dover for which the predictions are given. Tidal stream directions are given in degrees (True), e.g. 000° indicates N-going, 090°, E-going, 180°, S-going, 270°, W-going. Spring rates are in the column headed Sp. and neap rates are under Np, and are in knots.

Example: Assume that the direction and rate of the stream is required off Dover at 0400 GMT on June 16.

The time and height of the nearest HW at Dover is first taken from the Tide Tables (see Table 3.5).

ENGLAND, SOUTH COAST - DOVER

LAT 51°07'N   LONG 1°19'E

TIME ZONE GMT (see note below)   TIMES AND HEIGHTS OF HIGH AND LOW WATERS

APRIL				MAY				JUNE				JULY			
TIME	M	TIME	M	TIME	M	TIME	M	TIME	M	TIME	M	TIME	M	TIME	M
1 0059	6.7	**16** 0022	6.5	**1** 0112	6.4	**16** 0048	6.4	**1** 0158	5.8	**16** 0236	6.2	**1** 0218	5.8	**16** 0310	6.2
0839	0.6	0754	0.7	0833	1.0	0818	0.8	0917	1.5	1000	1.2	0931	1.6	1045	1.2
F 1319	6.4	SA 1243	6.4	SU 1331	6.1	M 1321	6.3	W 1423	5.8	TH 1500	6.2	F 1440	5.9	SA 1529	6.3
2046	0.9	2006	0.8	2044	1.2	2039	0.9	2138	1.6	2227	1.0	2156	1.6	2309	1.1
2 0137	6.5	**17** 0057	6.4	**2** 0145	6.1	**17** 0137	6.2	**2** 0242	5.5	**17** 0332	6.0	**2** 0305	5.6	**17** 0404	6.0
0907	0.9	0827	0.8	0905	1.2	0903	1.0	0956	1.8	1059	1.3	1009	1.8	1134	1.5
SA 1357	6.2	SU 1323	6.3	M 1406	5.9	TU 1413	6.1	TH 1510	5.6	F 1556	6.0	SA 1528	5.8	SU 1624	6.1
2112	1.1	2044	0.9	2119	1.4	2128	1.1	2221	1.8	2327	1.2	2238	1.7		
3 0215	6.2	**18** 0137	6.2	**3** 0222	5.7	**18** 0234	6.0	**3** 0341	5.2	**18** 0435	5.8	**3** 0402	5.4	**18** 0003	1.3
0936	1.2	0907	1.0	0941	1.6	0956	1.3	1041	2.0	1204	1.5	1054	1.9	0505	5.8
SU 1436	5.8	M 1408	6.0	TU 1447	5.6	W 1508	5.9	F 1609	5.4	SA 1659	5.9	SU 1623	5.6	M 1229	1.7
2145	1.5	2128	1.2	2159	1.8	2224	1.3	2313	2.0			2329	1.9	1729	5.9

Table 3.5

The nearest time shown is 0236 GMT and the height is 6·2m above chart datum. The height of the next LW after 0400 is 1·2m so that the range of that particular tide is 6·2 − 1·2 equal to 5·0m. The time of HW Dover is now compared with the time for which information is required, and the interval from HW found. In this example 0400 is 1 hour 24 minutes after HW at Dover. If the chart (Fig. 3.3) is now examined in the vicinity of Dover Harbour, the symbol ⟨P⟩ will be seen, indicating that predictions for that position are given in column P. On looking at this it will be seen that predictions for intervals after HW Dover are in the lower half of the table, and that for 1 hour after HW the direction and rates given are 064°, 4·1 knots at Springs, 2·3 knots at Neaps. For 2 hours after HW predictions are 066°, 3·5 knots at Springs, 1·9 knots at Neaps.

The interval for which predictions are required is approximately halfway between those given above, so that by averaging these predictions the required direction and rates obtained are 065°, 3·8 knots at Springs, 2·1 knots at Neaps.

The rate for the day in question is found by comparing the Range of the tide on that day with the Spring or Neap range as appropriate, taken from Table 3·6 marked on the chart, or found in Tide Tables.

Tidal Levels referred to Datum of Soundings

Place	Lat N	Long E	Heights in metres above datum				Datum and Remarks
			MHWS	MHWN	MLWN	MLWS	
Dover	51°07'	1°19	6·7	5·3	2·0	0·8	3 67m below Ordnance Datum (Newlyn)
Deal	51 13	1 25	6·1	5·0	2·0	0·8	3 40m below Ordnance Datum (Newlyn)
Richborough	51 18	1 21	3·3	2·7	0·3	0·1	1 33m below Ordnance Datum (Newlyn)
Ramsgate	51 20	1 25	4·9	3·8	1·2	0·4	2 58m below Ordnance Datum (Newlyn)
Broadstairs	51 21	1 27	4·6	3·7	1·3	0·4	2 35m below Ordnance Datum (Newlyn)
Margate	51 24	1 23	4·8	3·9	1·4	0·5	2 50m below Ordnance Datum (Newlyn)

Reproduced from British Admiralty Chart No. 1828 with the permission of the Controller of H.M. Stationery Office and the Hydrographer of the Navy.

Table 3.6

Reproduced from British Admiralty Chart No. 1828 with the permission of the Controller of H.M. Stationery Office and of the Hydrographer of the Navy.

Fig. 3.3

At Dover the Spring range is $6.7 - 0.8$m which gives 5.9m. The Neap range is $5.3 - 2.0$ which is 3.3m. If the range on the day had been nearly 5.9m (Springs) the rate would have been taken at 3.8 knots; if nearly 3.3m (Neaps) it would have been taken as 2.1 knots.

The rate for a day other than at Springs or Neaps is found by dividing the actual range on the day by the Spring range and multiplying the answer by the Spring rate of stream.

In this example, the information available is:
Spring range from chart 5.9 metres: actual range 16 June 5.0m; Spring rate 3.8 knots.
Therefore the rate required is $5.0/5.9 \times 3.8$ knots, which equals 3.2 knots. The predicted direction and rate of the stream off Dover at 0400 on June 16 is therefore $065°$T at 3.2 knots.

Note: As previously mentioned, **slack water does not necessarily coincide with the time of HW or LW** at a place. Although position P on chart 1828 is less than one mile from Dover Harbour, it can be seen from Table P that when it is HW there the stream is setting at 3.9 knots at springs and 2.2 knots at neaps.

THE TIDAL STREAM ATLASES   The Admiralty publish various pocket atlases, which between them cover most of the coastline of the British Isles. Reproductions of many of these, to a smaller scale, are in Reed's and other Almanacs.

A part of one of the charts contained in the Atlas for The Solent and Adjacent Waters is reproduced in Fig. 3.4. Each atlas contains thirteen small chartlets, with the information displayed in a similar manner. Each chart shows the directions and rates of the streams in all parts of the area at the time marked upon it. The directions of the streams are indicated by arrows. If the direction is required at a particular position in degrees, it can be estimated by eye, or found by drawing a meridian from top to bottom of the chart through the position, and measuring the angle between it and the nearest arrow. Rates are marked close to the arrow for which the information is given, in tenths of a knot for neaps and springs.

For example, 5 hours before HW at Portsmouth, the stream off Hurst Point is marked as $\underrightarrow{19.39}$. This indicates a neap rate of 1.9 knots and a spring rate of 3.9 knots at that position, and the direction is approximately $060°$. The *actual* rate on the day concerned is found in a similar manner to that described for the tables on charts, or by using the simple graph at the front of the atlas. The times for which the predictions are given are found by adding or subtracting the relevant

Reproduced from British Admiralty Pocket Tidal Stream Atlas (N.P. 337) with the permission of the Controller of H.M. Stationery Office and of the Hydrographer of the Navy.

Fig. 3.4

time intervals marked on the charts to the times of HW at the Standard Port on the day in question. These times, for one or more days if necessary, can then be marked in pencil on their appropriate charts, so that the atlas can be used when planning or making a passage without constantly referring to the Tide Tables. If an atlas is to be used on a passage this preparation can be done before the boat leaves port.

STANFORD'S TIDAL ATLASES Stanford Maritime Ltd. publish tidal stream atlases for the English Channel. They provide predictions of tidal streams and heights at ports in the area, and also show at a glance whether the tide is rising or falling, and how far it has yet to go. This feature is unique to Stanford's Tidal Stream Atlases.

The East and West Channel Atlases show tidal information for each hour before, at and after HW Dover. Having the times and heights of HW Dover for the day concerned, a conversion table in the Atlases gives a good prediction of the stream rate in knots. Left-hand pages show stream direction and mean rate. Right-hand pages give a very quick-to-use visual gauge of vertical movement of the tide, and using the tables given one can quickly obtain the approx. height at that time at any of 30 or so English and Continental ports.

Stanford's Central Channel Atlas is based on the time and height of HW at Cherbourg, which is given in Reed's and other almanacs. Otherwise it is used the same way.

Chapter 4

Navigational Equipment

Many of the aids used when navigating in narrow channels and estuaries have been described. Sufficient has probably already been written to enable a person with good eyesight and suitable charts to navigate in these areas in good visibility by working from buoy to buoy, identifying each in turn and then looking ahead for the next.

In these areas in poor visibility, and when longer coastal and sea passages are to be made, certain instruments and equipment will be required to allow the boat's position to be plotted on the chart, and to enable her to be steered from place to place.

CHART TABLE A flat board should be provided to act as a chart table, with minimum dimensions 22in athwartships by 30in fore and aft, but larger if possible. This can be made of ¼in or ⅜in ply, braced and stiffened so that it does not warp, and either portable so that it can be stowed in port, or hinged at the boat's side so that it can be folded up when not in use. There is no fixed size for Admiralty Charts when open, but all when folded will fit into a space 20in × 28in. If the table is made in the form of a box to this minimum size, and 1in or so deep, the space beneath the table can be used for stowing charts not in use. The table should be securely fixed when in use, and if possible a small seat should be arranged opposite to it, so that the navigator can get his knees under the table and brace himself against the boat's movement. There should be a light over the table. Holders or racks should be arranged near the table for a parallel ruler, pencils, dividers, rubbers and the various publications which have to be used.

PARALLEL RULERS are made of Perspex, boxwood or brass, and are either bar type or roller type. A suitable rule for a small chart table would be 15in long. An index is marked at the middle of one edge, and the other edge and the two ends are graduated in degrees anti-clockwise from 000° to 179°, with secondary marking from 180° to 359°. A parallel ruler is used for drawing, or laying-off on the chart

Fig. 4.1

courses and bearings, or for measuring courses. Its method of use will be described later.

THE DOUGLAS COMBINED PROTRACTOR AND PARALLEL RULE is made from transparent plastic in two sizes, 5in square and 10in square. As can be seen in Fig. 4.1 it is a square protractor, graduated from 000° to 359° both clockwise and anticlockwise. Pencil lines may be drawn on its underside which has a matt surface. It can be used instead of a parallel ruler for laying off or reading off courses and bearings, and instructions for use are supplied with it. It is less likely to be damaged than a parallel ruler, and is cheaper.

DIVIDERS are required for measuring distances on a chart. Those most suitable are made of brass with steel points, and should be at least 4in long. A pair of drawing compasses is also useful for marking in the ranges of various lights and for plotting position circles.

PENCILS AND RUBBERS More than one pencil should be carried, preferably B grade and hexagonal, and two or three small soft rubbers.

LOGBOOK A stiff-covered exercise book can be used as a logbook for recording courses steered, positions, weather, and any important events which occur. A small pad or notebook for noting bearings and other readings should also be carried.

THE MAGNETIC COMPASS indicates the direction of compass north and when suitably graduated other directions relative to compass north can be obtained. It consists of a graduated or marked card secured to a hemispherical float to which are attached two parallel tubular cases containing magnetised needles, or a ring magnet magnetised along one diameter. The centre of the float rests on a hardened pin centred at the bottom of a bowl filled with a mixture of ethyl alcohol and distilled water. A wire or painted lubber line inside the bowl indicates the direction in which the boat is heading. There is a filling plug on one side to allow the bowl to be topped up when necessary. The bowl is supported in gimbals in a brass binnacle so that it always remains horizontal. Two diametrically opposite marks are engraved on the outside of the binnacle so that it can be lined up correctly in the boat. A hood is often fitted to protect the card from sunlight, and some form of lighting is desirable.

Many compasses are gimballed internally and filled with a low drag spirit to damp the card's movement. The bowl may be suspended from a bracket instead of being fitted in a binnacle.

GRADUATION OF COMPASS CARDS Compasses sold specifically for use in yachts usually have their cards graduated every 2°, or alternatively every 5° for clarity. They can be manufactured in black with white markings, or white with black markings. Many are also marked with the cardinal and inter-cardinal headings N, NE, E, SE etc and a few may still be met marked in points and half and/or quarter points (Fig. 4.2). The three possible methods are described below in the order in which they are likely to be met.

The Three Figure Method. When using this method a direction is always described in terms of three figures, and the card is graduated in degrees clockwise from 000° (N) through 090° (E), 180° (S) and 270° (W) to 359°. The direction SE would be 135°. This is the simplest and most accurate method of describing a direction, and its use is recommended.

The Quadrantal Method. This method uses the cardinal points and degrees to describe a direction. The four quadrants of the card are each divided into 90 degrees, with zero at N and S, and 90 at E and

Fig. 4.2 Compass card graduated in points and quarter points, and every 5°; in the 'three figure' notation, the last 0 at each ten degree mark being omitted to allow larger figures to be used

W. The four cardinal directions are described simply as N, E, S, or W, while intermediate directions are named from N or S towards E or W. The direction SE for example, would be described S45°E.

The Point Method. Because the complete card contains four right angles or 360°, and is divided into 32 points, one point is $11\frac{1}{4}°$. On many cards each point is further divided into half points ($5\frac{5}{8}°$), and quarter points ($2\frac{13}{16}°$). A conversion table is contained in Reed's Nautical Almanac, enabling a course given in degrees to be changed into points and quarter points, or vice versa. Some hand bearing compasses are marked in quarter points as well as degrees.

Compass Types
STEERING COMPASSES A steering compass is required and must be placed in the boat so that the card and lubber line can be seen clearly by the helmsman. In boats fitted with wheel steering this is fairly easily achieved by placing a compass with a normal card on a

Fig. 4.3 A selection of compasses: *A*. Radiant hand bearing compass, *B*. Major binnacle compass, *C*. grid compass (Henry Browne & Son). *D*. is the smaller Mini Compass (Offshore Instruments). *A* and *D* have beta lights, and all four use 360° notation.

pedestal or bracket forward of the wheel. A magnifying prism or glass can sometimes be fitted to enlarge the lubber line and adjacent portion of the card.

Some cards are graduated at every 2° and others at every 5°, to make the graduations clearer. In a yacht steered by a tiller, the helmsman may have to move from side to side, and may not be able to see clearly the card of a compass placed over the boat's keel. The proper course may not be steered when the compass is viewed from one side, because of parallax. With tiller steering, a grid type steering compass placed under the tiller is often more convenient and easier to steer by. There are two types of grid compass, but both are used in the same manner. One type has a normal compass card, with the addition of a red wire attached to the top of the card and passing through the N and S points. The lubber line runs across the diameter of the bowl, beneath the glass. A rotatable grid ring graduated from 0° to 359° with a parallel wire on each side of the 0°–180° direction, is fitted on top of the compass bowl. (See Fig. 4.4.) To point or head the boat in

Red N–S Wire. Lubber Line

Lubber Line (white)

Heading 090°
Grid set to 090°

Heading 090°
Grid set to 135°
ready for course alteration

Heading 135°

GRID COMPASSES

Fig. 4.4

a particular direction, the following method is used. Assuming for example, that the boat is to be headed 135° (SE), the grid ring is first rotated until the 135° graduation on the ring is in line with the forward end of the lubber line, and is then clamped to the bowl. The boat is then turned until the grid wires lie parallel to, and each side of, the red N–S wire on the card with the N mark on the grid ring immediately over the N end of the red wire. The boat will then be heading 135° (SE), and can easily be kept heading in that direction by keeping the grid wires parallel to the red wire on the card, even when the compass is viewed from one side. The other type of grid compass was primarily designed for use in aircraft, but a large number of these have been sold to the public as surplus Government stores. The card is black, and is marked with two white lines in the E–W direction, and at right angles to these a further white line to indicate the direction of N. The grid ring is graduated in degrees from 000° to 359°, and white grid wires are fitted to it in the form of an inverted T as shown. The boat is headed in the required direction by turning and clamping the grid ring as before, and then turning the boat until the grid wires lie each side of the white lines on the card.

Note: When turning a boat so that she heads in a particular direction, it must always be remembered that the boat, and hence the compass bowl and lubber line, *turns round the card.* The compass card does *not* move, beyond being deflected by deviation, although it will appear to move.

THE HAND BEARING COMPASS In most small yachts it is not possible to place the steering compass in a position suitable for taking the bearings required to fix the boat's position. It is therefore usual to carry a separate hand bearing compass for this purpose. The type shown at *A* in Fig. 4.3 must have the prism adjusted correctly so that the reflected image of the card can be seen against the object when viewed horizontally across the bowl. The bearing is then noted in the prism where the engraved line cuts the reflected image of the card. Modern designs like that shown at *D* are smaller and lighter and can be slung round the neck or kept in a pocket ready for use. The optics of these instruments are often designed to eliminate parallax errors.

A hand bearing compass should be kept at least four feet away from the steering compass. Taking bearings requires practice, and the instrument should be kept well clear of steel or iron fittings as a bearing is taken.

TOWED LOGS The simplest log, made by Thomas Walker & Son Ltd, is used to measure the distance sailed through the water. It is entirely mechanical and requires no electrical supply. A rotator is attached to one end of a braided line the other end of which is hooked to a register which records the distance. The register fits into a shoe on to the boat's transom, and the rotator is towed astern by the line. Each mile sailed through the water is registered after the rotator has made a fixed number of revolutions as it is towed through the water. The length of line required for accurate registration of distance depends on the height of the register above the water and the maximum speed of the boat; recommendations as to length are supplied by the manu-facturers. A sinker keeps the rotator immersed in the water (Fig. 4.5).

Fig. 4.5

These logs register distance sailed through the water accurately at speeds above $2-2\frac{1}{2}$ knots in fine weather, but tend to under-register at speeds below 2 knots and when running before a heavy sea. They tend tend to over-register in strong winds from ahead or on the bow. By converting the register to a generator, it can be made to indicate speed through the water on a suitably calibrated meter.

To take in the log, known as 'handing the log', first unhook the line from the register and then pay out this end over the transom as the rotator is hauled in, to avoid getting turns in the line. Once the rotator is inboard the line can be hauled in free of turns.

The Stowe trailing log has a rotator which is towed at the end of a 10 metre non-rotating cable. The speed of rotation of the rotator is converted electrically to indicate speed on a meter and distance on a counter. It is claimed to have a high resistance to fouling by weed, but is easily cleared if fouled because the cable does not rotate.

PRESSURE LOGS measure speed through the water, and in some logs the speed information can be integrated to provide distance through the water. One type consists of two vertical tubes, side by side, both open at their lower ends and immersed in the sea below the hull. One tube has its open end pointing forward, and both open ends are at the same pressure when the boat is stopped. When making way through the water the pressure in the forward-facing tube is increased and the difference in pressure between the two tubes operates a meter calibrated to indicate speed. Another type has a spring-loaded needle inserted through a fitting in the bottom of the hull. When stopped the needle is vertical, but when the boat is moving through the water the pressure applied to the needle hinges it through an arc towards the stern. This motion is proportional to the boat's speed, and the instrument's output is applied to speed and distance meters.

IMPELLER LOGS consist of a screw-type impeller mounted at the tip of a streamlined fin projecting about 3in through a hull fitting in the bottom. This fitting usually includes a valve to enable the unit to be withdrawn for maintenance or to prevent damage on grounding. A weed deflector is fitted in line with the impeller.

The impeller contains a magnet and as this is rotated by the boat's forward motion its rotating field induces small pulses of current in a coil in the underwater unit. The pulses are fed by screened cable to an electronic counter which produces a record of distance sailed each one hundredth of a mile after a designed number of pulses. The rate of arrival of the pulses from the impeller is measured, converted to a proportional current and applied to a speed meter. Other designs use a small paddle wheel instead of an impeller to produce the same result, with, it is claimed, less fouling by weed. In another design a non-retractable impeller is linked to the speed and distance meter by a cable which transmits the impeller's revolutions directly to the meter in the same way as the log line in the towed log (or a car's speedometer cable).

It is important to try to site the impeller clear of turbulent water. For sailing yachts and displacement powerboats, a position about one-third of waterline length from the forward end of the waterline, and 30cm (12in) away from the centreline, has often been found to be satisfactory. Sailing yachts may require an impeller on each side for best results, with a gravity-operated switch selecting the signals from the lee side unit automatically. High speed powerboats may need the impeller fitted one-quarter of length from aft, and the mechanical log may also have to be sited in the after part of the hull.

Fig. 4.6

This type of instrument once calibrated and adjusted should measure speed through the water within about $\pm 5\%$ of speed from 0·7 knot upwards, and distance within $\pm 2\%$ of distance run through the water.

CALIBRATION All logs measure distance and/or speed *through the water*, which is not necessarily the same as distance or speed *over the ground*. They require calibration and this can be done by making two runs in opposite directions over a measured distance when the tidal stream is negligible or constant. The percentage log error is given by

the expression $100 \left[\dfrac{V_1 + V_2}{L_1 + L_2} - 1 \right]$ where:

V_1 and V_2 are the actual observed speeds over the ground for each run, and L_1 and L_2 are the speeds indicated by the log for each run. This error is not necessarily constant over the whole range of boat speeds, and if possible should be checked at other speeds. The error can be used to apply a correction to any reading obtained, or used to adjust the instrument by means of a calibration control provided by the manufacturers until the error is negligible.

THE DUTCHMAN'S LOG can be used to estimate the boat's speed when it is so low that instruments are inaccurate. The speed can be found by calculation, by observing the time taken for the boat to pass a floating and stationary object close alongside. This can be done by throwing some small buoyant object ahead and to one side of the boat, and then noting the times when first the stem, and then the transom, pass it. If a table has been previously worked out, based on the boat's overall length, the speed can be obtained by inspection from the table by entering it with the time interval observed. To draw up such a table, multiply the overall length of the boat (in feet) by 3600 (the number of seconds in 1 hour), and divide the product by 6080 (feet in 1 nautical mile). The answer gives the speed in knots appropriate to a time interval of 1 second. By dividing this figure in turn by 2, 3, 4, 5, etc the speed appropriate for each of these time intervals (in seconds) can be obtained, and then drawn up in a table.

Example. For a boat with overall length of 20 feet.

$$\text{Speed for a time interval of 1 sec.} = \frac{20 \times 3600}{6080}$$
$$= 11 \cdot 8 \text{ knots.}$$

DUTCHMAN'S LOG TABLE

Interval (Secs.)	Speed (Knots)	Interval (Secs.)	Speed (Knots)
2	5·9	6	2·0
3	3·9	7	1·7
4	3·0	8	1·5
5	2·4	9	1·3
		and so on	

SOUNDING The simplest method of taking quick soundings in shallow water is to use a long boathook or a bamboo cane weighted at one end. These can be marked in feet by painting alternate foot lengths with black or white paint. Boats sailing frequently in shallow creeks and rivers often carry such a sounding pole secured in the rigging ready for instant use.

A Lead and Line should be carried for sounding in less shallow water. It consists of a 7lb lead or weight secured to the end of a 25 metre length of line (about 6–7mm diameter). The line should have a long eye spliced in one end and should then be wetted and stretched. It should then be marked from the end of the eye splice by tucking the following material through the strands of the line:

At 2m – two strips of leather
At 3 and 13m – a piece of blue bunting
At 5 and 15 metres – a piece of white bunting
At 7 and 17 metres – a piece of red bunting
At 10 metres – a piece of leather with a hole in it
At 20 metres – a piece of leather with a hole in it
    and two leather strips.

The line is bent to the lead by passing the eye splice through the becket on the lead, and then passing the lead through the eye and pulling tight. When a sounding is required with the boat underway, the lead is hove ahead of the boat from the weather side, and the sounding read off when the line is up and down with the lead on the bottom. In deep water the boat may have to be hove to for a short time while the sounding is obtained. The line is best kept on a small reel when not in use.

ECHO SOUNDERS suitable for yachts can be designed to work from internal batteries or from the main supply of 12 to 36 volts.

A yacht installation consists of the depth display, a rotating LED (light-emitting diode) within a scale or a meter and pointer, the transmitting unit and a transducer in the bottom of the hull.

The principle of all echo sounders requires the instrument to measure the time taken for a short pulse to travel from the hull transducer to the seabed and back. The time interval and hence the depth can be measured by using an arm which rotates at constant speed within the scale and holds a neon bulb or LED at one end. As it passes zero on the scale it flashes and also triggers the transmitting unit which applies a high frequency electrical pulse to the transducer, where it is converted into an ultrasonic sound pulse. This sound pulse is injected downwards into the sea where it travels at a constant velocity of 1500m per sec (4920 ft per sec), strikes the seabed and is returned as a weak echo at the same velocity to be 'received' by the

| Transmission | Pulse reaches seabed echo starts back | Echo reaches transducer Light flashes |

HOW THE ECHO SOUNDER WORKS

Fig. 4.7

transducer. This converts the weak echo sound pulse back to an electrical pulse which is amplified and applied to the LED on the rotating arm, which has moved round to a point proportional to the time taken for the pulse to travel down and back. The pulse causes a flash at this point, which indicates the depth against the scale. The scale is calibrated to show depth, which is half the total distance travelled by the pulse in the time interval, as shown by the expression:

Depth (m) = vt ÷ 2 where v is velocity of sound in salt water (m/sec) and t is time interval for pulse out and echo back (secs).

As the pulses are made at a rapid rate, e.g. 400 per minute for deep soundings, and 2400 per minute for shallow, on one instrument, the LED flashes appear as a continuous bright line at zero and at the measured depth.

In instruments using meter and pointer presentation, the time difference between transmission of a pulse and reception of its echo is measured by electronic circuits which deliver a current to the meter proportional to the time difference and hence to the water depth.

Another type of echo sounder records the depth on sensitised paper by applying the electrical pulse created by the returning echo to a stylus which moves across the paper at a constant rate. The pulse burns away the surface of the paper at the appropriate place to leave a black line which is compared with a depth scale to obtain the sounding. The paper is made to move slowly so that a continuous record is obtained.

Sailing yachts should ideally be fitted with two transducers, one on each side of the keel, and with an automatic gravity switch to connect the lee side (deeper) transducer to the indicator. Aeration of the water immediately beneath the transducer may completely prevent sounding, and to avoid this, special transducers with project 50mm (2in) or more below the outer surface of the hull can be obtained, together with a fairing block. Transducers should generally be sited about one-third of length from forward, but in some power boats better results may be obtained when sited one-quarter of length from aft. All should be clear of any hull projections which may cause turbulence and aeration of the water, e.g. struts or discharges.

The usual presentation shows soundings up to 120m or 60 fathoms, with an accuracy of about 2% of depth. The minimum sounding which can be obtained is usually about 0·8m or 2·7ft. A control is often provided for adjustment to allow for the fact that the transducer is below sea level and enable the true depth of water to be displayed.

When the sounder is operating in deeper water than the maximum

Fig. 4.8   This Seafarer 700 echosounder has both LED and digital depth displays, and several interesting features such as three range choices for different depths, shallow and deep water alarms, and a facility for minimising current consumption by using the digital LCD only. (Seafarer Navigation International Ltd)

of the scale provided, e.g. sounding in 120m with maximum scale for one revolution of 100m, and if the sea bed is hard, it is possible for an echo to be returned to the transducer after the next pulse has been transmitted. In these circumstances a sounding may be indicated at 20m with the rotating arm making its next revolution. The time measured will be proportional to $1\frac{1}{5}$ revolutions so that the real depth indicated is 120m. Such echoes are called 'second trace' echoes and they can be removed by decreasing gain. If they occur when using the sounder on shallow setting, e.g. sounding in 24m, maximum of scale 20m, sounder showing 4m, changing the Range switch to deep will usually confirm the proper depth which would then show as 24m on a 0 to 100m scale.

Fish, layers of water of differing salinity, and layers of plankton may also return echoes above the bottom echoes. In some circumstances they can completely mask the bottom echo.

RADIO RECEIVERS AND DIRECTION-FINDERS A radio receiver is of great value aboard a yacht as it can be used to obtain weather forecasts. An ordinary portable set is not usually suitable for use at sea because it is liable to be damaged by sea air and damp, nevertheless it would be better to carry one of this type (provided it can receive on the Long Wave Band) rather than none at all. If it can be enclosed in a plastic covering and connected to a vertical aerial, it will probably give reasonable reception.

A number of small portable sets are made which combine the functions of radio receivers and direction-finders. They operate off their own batteries and are designed for use in small craft. When connected to a vertical aerial (an insulated copper wire run up the

Fig. 4.9   Hand-held radio direction finders (RDFs). These self-contained portable sets incorporate aerial, receiver, batteries, compass for taking bearings of radiobeacons, and earphones which cut out extraneous noise. They will receive marine, aero and Consol beacons, and long wave broadcasts. From left, they are the Seafix and Seafix 2000 (Seafarer Navigation International Ltd).

Fig. 4.10 Hand-held RDF sets with liquid crystal displays (LCDs) of frequency to assist tuning, and internal batteries rechargeable from the ship's electrical supply. Earphones and null indicator light are not shown. The sets are the Lokata 5 (left), and the 5B which has a timer used in identifying radiobeacons which transmit in sequence on the same frequency. (Lokata Instruments)

The Lokata SSB/RX is a related equipment in which the RDF function is coupled with a radio receiver that covers LW, MW, SW and FM bands and will receive marine SSB transmissions. It operates from the ship's supply, and the photo shows the null meter, digital frequency display and beacon timer lights. (Lokata Instruments)

mast is suitable) they can receive the weather forecasts for shipping broadcast by the BBC.

As direction finders these receivers are usually hand-held radio bearing compasses (Fig. 4.9). The RDF instrument incorporates a horizontal ferrite rod aerial which produces a null (silent area) when pointed towards the radiobeacon, and a bearing compass to indicate the bearing when the aerial is in the null position. The procedure for taking radio bearings is described in Chapter 7.

MARITIME VHF RADIOTELEPHONE FACILITIES Yachtsmen wishing to communicate with each other or with harbour authorities can do so by fitting Very High Frequency (VHF) radiotelephone (RT) equipment capable of transmitting and receiving in the Maritime VHF Band (156–174 MHz). Although this equipment is limited to approximately line-of-sight range, it can be very helpful during an approach to receive from the port authorities traffic control or berthing instructions, and information about facilities or other craft leaving or entering. A VHF receiver can also, to a limited extent, be used to obtain a position line when in the vicinity of VHF Radio Lighthouses (see Chapter 7).

VHF DIRECTION-FINDING STATIONS A number of HM Coastguard stations operate direction-finding antennae around the U.K. coasts from which **in an emergency** the bearings of craft within range and transmitting on VHF can be obtained. **On request from a boat in distress** the Coastguard station will transmit from the direction-finding site the bearing of the boat FROM the direction-finding antenna. These stations are marked RG Stations on BA charts and are listed in the Admiralty List of Radio Services for Small Craft after the radiobeacons in the Great Britain section. Transmission is on Ch 16 (distress only) or Ch 67.

Chapter 5

Compass Errors and Corrections

Errors of the Compass

It is first necessary to understand the meaning of the following terms:

THE BOAT'S HEAD or HEADING describes the direction in which the boat is pointing at any particular time. It does not necessarily have to be in motion.

THE COURSE or TRACK describes the direction in which the boat is being, or is to be, steered.

A BEARING is the direction of one position from another position.

Each of these directions can be described by referring it to the direction of one of the following datum lines through the boat's position:

1. the True Meridian, whose direction is described as True North.
2. the Magnetic Meridian, whose direction is described as Magnetic North.
3. the axis of the Compass needles, whose direction is described as Compass North.

Hence directions referred to in:

1. are true courses and bearings, indicated by the suffix T.
2. are magnetic courses and bearings, indicated by the suffix M.
3. are compass courses and bearings, indicated by the suffix C.

These are usually given in degrees in 360° notation, e.g. 060°T means a direction 60° to the right of true north.

075°M means a direction 75° to the right of magnetic north.

135°C means a direction 135° to the right of compass north.

In a boat out of sight of land, the horizon appears as a circle with the boat at its centre, and there is nothing to distinguish one point on that circle from another. In order to head the boat in a particular direction, and then to keep her heading in that direction, it is necessary to refer to some datum line or reference point.

This is supplied by the N–S line on the compass card, the N point indicating the direction of compass north. Compass north does not generally lie in the same direction as true north because of the errors of Variation and Deviation which will now be described.

VARIATION If a compass is placed in a boat constructed entirely of non-magnetic materials so that the compass needles are influenced by the earth's magnetic field and no other, the card will steady with its N–S line in the direction of the magnetic meridian through the boat's position, with the N point of the card towards magnetic north. The magnetic and true meridians at a place do not generally coincide, because the earth's magnetic field is irregular, and the earth's N and S magnetic poles do not coincide with the geographical poles. The magnetic poles are areas about 50 miles in diameter which are constantly moving in unpredictable paths because the earth's magnetic field is continuously changing. The North magnetic pole is in the Canadian Arctic.

The angle, expressed in degrees and minutes of arc, between the true and magnetic meridians at a given place is called the Variation. It is named Easterly when the direction of magnetic north lies to the East or right of the true meridian, and Westerly when to the West or left of the true meridian.

Because of the movement of the magnetic poles, the variation at any place is not constant but changes slowly year by year. In practice the navigator obtains the variation for a specified year, and its rate of change, either from the coastal chart which he is using or from a special chart which has Isogonic Lines drawn through all positions which have equal variation.

On coastal charts this information is given across one of the axes of the compass roses. A part of one of the special charts covering the British Isles and Europe is given in Reed's Nautical Almanac, and shown in Fig. 5.1. The isogonic lines are those trending roughly N–S in this region, and the variation is W almost throughout the whole of the area shown. On the eastern edge is the Agonic Line, or line through places where variation is zero, and to the east of that, in the eastern Baltic, the variation is E. The wider lines trending roughly N–S are called Isallogonic Lines and they are drawn through all places where the annual change of variation is constant. It can be seen from these lines that the Westerly variation in the British Isles is now decreasing by between 8′ and 10′ annually.

Variation is found by first plotting the boat's position on this chart, and then taking the value from the nearest isogonic line. If the position comes between two lines, the value can be estimated by eye to the nearest half degree. This value is then corrected by adding or subtracting

Fig. 5.1   Magnetic variation in 1980 indicated by Isogonic Lines (°W)
and annual change by Isallogonic Lines ('E). (Reed's Nautical
Almanac)

the change of variation, found by multiplying the rate of change in
minutes of arc by the difference in years between the specified and
current year.

DEVIATION If a magnetic compass is placed in a boat constructed
of steel or ferrocement, or near iron and steel fittings, or the engine in
a boat constructed of non-magnetic materials, the compass needle will
almost certainly be deflected from the magnetic meridian through the

boat's position, and the card will steady with its N point towards the direction known as Compass North. The angle between the directions of Magnetic N and Compass N is called the Deviation. If compass North lies to the East or right of magnetic north, deviation is named Easterly: if it lies to the west or left, deviation is named Westerly. Deviation can also be caused in any boat if equipment such as loudspeakers, earphones, ammeters etc, which contain magnets, are placed too close to the compass.

Any iron or steel in a boat is partly magnetised by the earth's magnetic field during construction, and is further magnetised after launching. The boat itself therefore acquires a magnetic field which unfortunately partly changes its direction and strength as the boat is turned onto different headings.

Deviation is caused by the boat's magnetic field acting at an angle to the compass needles, and because this angle and the strength of the boat's field change as the boat turns on to different headings, the deviation also changes with change of heading. It is therefore necessary to find the deviation when the boat is on each of a number of different headings, so that the correct deviation can be allowed for when setting a course from one position to another.

One method of carrying out 'a swing for deviation' is described below. It requires the use of a separate hand bearing compass and could be used in boats where it is impossible to take bearings from the steering compass because it is below the cockpit coaming.

SWINGING FOR DEVIATION Before carrying out the swing, all movable iron, steel and electrical equipment should be stowed in its sea-going position, and as far away from the compass as possible.

The steering compass should be fixed, if possible, with its centre not less than the following distances from magnetic material:

Fixed magnetic material and other compasses	4 ft
Magnetic material occasionally moved	6 ft
Switches, headphones, loudspeakers, ammeters and other instruments containing small magnets	3 ft
Electric wiring should be twin-flex type if passing near the compass.	

The compass should be fixed so that the two marks on the binnacle are in, or parallel to, the boat's fore-and-aft line, with the lubber line on the fore side of the compass bowl.

A calm day should be chosen and the boat should be upright not heeled. She can be swung at anchor or on suitable moorings using extra lines run to a kedge anchor laid out astern, or better still on each quarter. The swing should be carried out at or near slack water if there is any tidal stream. A line should be stretched from the top of the mast (if only one) to the centre of the transom, or alternatively two vertical battens should be set up temporarily over the boat's fore-and-aft centreline, one forward and one aft. An assistant, with the hand bearing compass, should then be sent away in the dinghy after checking that it contains no iron or steel fittings. The dinghy should be positioned about three boat-lengths astern, and should adjust its position so that it remains astern of the boat throughout the swing. The boat is then slowly swung, adjusting the lines as necessary, and successively steadied on at least eight, but preferably sixteen, equidistant compass headings, e.g. say 000° (N), 045° (NE), 090° (E), and so on. As the boat is steadied and held on each heading, a previously agreed signal should be made to the dinghy and the assistant there should immediately take a bearing of the boat's mast with the hand bearing compass when he sees the line stretched from the mast in line with the centre of the mast. (If battens have been erected, this bearing should be taken when he sees them in line.) The assistant then notes the bearing on a pad, signals that he has taken the bearing, and the boat is swung onto the hext heading where the same routine is followed.

DEVIATION CURVE

Fig. 5.2

After the boat has been swung through 360°, which may have to be done in two parts if a strong tidal stream runs at the anchorage, the bearings taken from the dinghy should be compared with the corresponding compass headings of the boat noted during the swing. Each bearing taken from the dinghy can be assumed to be the *magnetic* heading of the boat at the time it was taken. The differences between corresponding *compass* (from the compass being corrected) and *magnetic* headings are the deviation on those headings, and they can be drawn up in a table (Table 5.1).

Table 5.1

Compass heading of boat		Deviation	Magnetic heading of boat
N	000°C	3° E	003° M
NE	045°C	5° E	050° M
E	090°C	5° E	095° M
SE	135°C	3° E	138° M
S	180°C	2° W	178° M
SW	225°C	6° W	219° M
W	270°C	6° W	264° M
NW	315°C	1° W	314° M

To name the deviations shown above, consider which way the steering compass card would have to be turned (deflected) to achieve its corresponding magnetic heading. This will decide whether compass N lies to the left or right of magnetic N and hence the name of the deviation.

Example. When the boat was heading 045°C, its magnetic heading was 050°M. To achieve a heading of 050° with the steering compass, the card would have to be turned to the left (anti-clockwise). Compass N must therefore lie to the right or E of magnetic N and the deviation must be E on this heading. Similarly when the boat was heading 270°C, its magnetic heading was 264°M, and the compass card would have to be turned to the right (clockwise) to achieve 264°. Compass N must therefore lie to the left or W of magnetic N and the deviation must be W on this heading.

These deviations can be plotted on graph paper to obtain a deviation curve as shown (Fig. 5.2). The curve can then be used to obtain the deviations on other intermediate compass headings, say every 10° or 20°, and these together with the corresponding magnetic headings can be drawn up in a table for use in the boat (Table 5.2).

Table 5.2

Compass	Deviation	Magnetic
000°C	3° E	003° M
020°C	4° E	024° M
040°C	5° E	045° M
060°C	5° E	065° M
080°C	5° E	085° M
100°C	5° E	105° M
120°C	4° E	124° M
140°C	3° E	143° M
160°C	Nil	160° M
180°C	2° W	178° M

Similar results can be obtained, perhaps more readily for a check swing, by using black plastic tape to make sighting marks on each side of the centre of the pulpit, in such a way that when viewed from right aft, the mast just fits between the marks when the observer is sighting directly along the fore-and-aft line. (If there is no pulpit, lash a sighting bar with two similar marks to the forestay.) If the boat is then put on successive headings, even moving about if necessary, and a bearing of the mast when it is centred between the marks is taken on each heading with the hand bearing compass held in as high a position as possible, a similar table to Table 5.2 can be prepared. The hand bearing compass observations would be assumed to be magnetic headings, and the equivalent compass headings taken with the boat's compass would need to be noted as before.

If the boat is fitted with an engine, it would be as well to carry out a second swing with the engine running to see if the deviations are different on any readings, and if they are, a second card should be drawn up for use when the engine is running.

In sailing craft which may be heeled appreciably for long periods when closehauled or reaching, the deviations on certain courses may differ from those obtained when upright. The amount of change through heeling of deviation on any heading is known as Heeling Error, and if present is maximum on N-S courses, and nil on E-W courses. It may be possible to detect heeling error by heeling the boat with weights hung from the boom squared off at right angles to the fore-and-aft line, heading her N or S by compass, and then finding the deviation when heeled with the hand bearing compass as before. Any difference between the deviations on equivalent headings when heeled and upright is the heeling error. It is impossible to allow for heeling error, but a compass adjuster can counteract the force that causes it with suitably placed vertical magnets. Similarly, a compass adjuster can reduce deviations found when upright by placing small correctors near to the compass. It will probably be essential to have the deviations reduced in this way in a steel or ferrocement yacht.

A boat should be swung at least once per season, preferably at the beginning of the season if she has been laid up during the winter. During the season the deviations should be checked when possible by comparing the compass heading when the boat is sailing down a suitable transit with the magnetic bearing obtained from the chart.

CORRECTION OF COURSES AND BEARINGS In practice the navigator has to work out the compass course to steer after he has obtained the required true or magnetic course from the chart. Alternatively, after steering a certain compass course for some time, he has to work out the corresponding magnetic or true course that was steered, so that he can estimate his position after allowing for the effects of wind and tidal stream. Similarly, compass bearings taken to fix the boat's position have to be converted into true or magnetic bearings before they can be drawn on the chart. To correct these various courses and bearings, the appropriate variation and deviation (if any) must be applied correctly, and to simplify this application all courses and bearings should be expressed in 360° notation.

TO FIND THE COMPASS COURSE TO STEER A pencil line is first drawn or laid off in the required direction from the boat's position on the chart, using the parallel rulers. These are then moved to the centre of the nearest compass rose. The true course is then read from where the rulers cut the outer circle of graduations, or the magnetic course from where the rulers cut the inner circle of graduations. It is advisable to use the outer true rose as it is clearer and easier to read, unless the boat's steering compass is marked only in points and half or quarter points. If this is the case the magnetic course can be read from the inner markings of the inner magnetic rose. If the navigator prefers to start with the magnetic course from the chart, this probably can be achieved most easily by drawing in waterproof coloured ink a series of magnetic meridians across the chart, each inclined to the true meridians by the appropriate variation for that area. He can then use the graduations on his parallel rules, Douglas protractor or other device to read, or lay off, magnetic courses and bearings directly against these magnetic meridians.

Fig. 5.3   Compass Roses, True and Magnetic

If the true course has been measured, it must be first converted to a magnetic course by applying the variation for the boat's position, after correcting it for any accumulated change of variation.

Example. In 1980 the variation off Poole was 6° 30′ W decreasing about 8½′ annually. What is the variation to use in this area in 1983? (Check above variation on Variation Chart, Fig. 5.1.)

The variation must be corrected for annual change, which here is 3 years at 8½′ per year equal to −25½′.

1980 variation	6° 30′ W	
3 years' change	−25½′	
1983 variation	6° W	(*High*)

The variation should be normally corrected to the nearest whole degree, and then named *High* if west, and *Low* if east. The correction can be usually made mentally. (Note: The reason for naming the above westerly variation *High* can be seen by looking at the compass rose (Fig. 5.3), where it can be seen that all the magnetic values are higher than their equivalent true values by the amount of the variation which is there shown as 12° W.)

It must be clearly understood that the value of the variation depends on the boat's geographical position and this is clearly shown on the variation chart in Fig. 5.1 where it can be seen that the variation off Stockholm, for example, is 1° E and changing a negligible amount each year.

Deviation must also be considered. To simplify its application, all easterly deviations in the table should be marked *Low* (East – least – *Low*) and all westerly deviations marked *High*. It can be seen in the deviation table (Table 5.1) that when the deviations are expressed in this way they indicate the number of degrees that the compass headings are either *Low* or *High* when compared with the corresponding magnetic headings. Therefore a *Low* variation should be subtracted from a true course to get a magnetic course, and a *Low* deviation subtracted from a magnetic course to get a compass course to steer. *High* variation and *High* deviation should be added to their respective headings to obtain magnetic and compass courses respectively.

The deviation is obtained from the table to the nearest degree by entering the column headed Magnetic with the magnetic course and estimating between successive values as necessary.

Example. Off Poole, and using the variation of 6° W (*High*) previously obtained, what compass course should be steered if the course obtained from the chart is 149° T and the deviation table is that shown in Fig. 5.2?

True course from chart	149° T
Variation corrected for annual change	+6° W (*High*)
Magnetic course to steer	155° M (Higher than T.)
Deviation from table (see note 1 below)	−1° E (*Low*)
Compass course to steer	154° C (Lower than M.)

Note 1: Deviation is 3° E (*Low*) on 143° M and *Nil* on 160° M, and it therefore changes 1° for approximately 6° change of heading. Because 155° M is 5° from 160° M, the deviation on 155° M differs by 1° from that on 160° M giving 1° E (*Low*).

Note 2: The order of application of variation and deviation when converting true to compass is:

True   Variation   Magnetic   Deviation Compass.

Note 3: Where variation is *High* the magnetic course is higher than true. Where deviation is *Low* the compass course is lower than magnetic, and vice-versa. In other words, **when error is high steer high, when low steer low**.

Note 4: The sum of variation and deviation is here 6° W (*High*) plus 1° E (*Low*) equal to 5° W (*High*), and is called the compass error. The compass course is therefore 5° higher than the true course.

TO FIND THE TRUE OR MAGNETIC COURSE STEERED AFTER STEERING A CERTAIN COMPASS COURSE

When a yacht is sailing as close to the wind as possible, first on one tack and then on the other, the average compass course steered on each tack must be noted by the helmsman, so that it can be converted into its corresponding true or magnetic course and laid off on the chart from the yacht's last known or estimated position. The appropriate deviation is obtained from the table to the nearest degree, by entering the column headed Compass with the compass course steered, and interpolating between successive values as necessary. If the deviation obtained is low, this indicates that the compass reading was low, and the deviation must be added to obtain the magnetic course steered; if high, this indicates that the compass reading was high, and it must be subtracted.

For those plotting using magnetic information, the track (magnetic course) can be now laid off from the last known position using the magnetic rose or magnetic meridian drawn on the chart.

In all other cases the corrected variation must be applied to the magnetic course in order to obtain the true course which has been steered. The parallel rules can then be laid across the nearest true rose at the appropriate true course and then moved to the boat's last position to draw in the track in degrees True.

Example. Off Dublin in 1982, steering 105° C, deviation as per Table 5.2, variation 9° 19′ W (1980) decreasing about $9\frac{1}{2}'$ annually. What is the track angle (True course) to lay off on the chart from the yacht's position?

By inspection of the deviation card, it can be seen that the deviation on 105°C is $4\frac{3}{4}$°E (*Low*), or 5°E (*Low*) to the nearest degree. The variation is 9° 19′ W less $2 \times 9\frac{1}{2}'$ per year equal to 19′, to give 9°W (*High*). The calculation is then:

Compass course steered	105° C	
Deviation (from table)	$+5°$ E (*Low*)	(Added because C is low compared to M)

Magnetic course steered	110° M	
Variation	−9° W (*High*)	(Subtracted because M is higher than T)
True course steered	101° T	= Track angle

Note 1: Order of application of errors is:
  Compass   Deviation   Magnetic   Variation   True.
Note 2: The compass error is 5° E (*Low*) plus 9° W (*High*) equal to 4° W (*High*). The Compass course is therefore 4° higher than the True course, and the error must be subtracted to give the True course.

BEARINGS   A hand bearing compass is usually used for taking bearings from small yachts as the steering compass is normally sited too low down in the boat. If the bearings are taken with the hand compass from a carefully chosen position on deck, as far away as possible from engine, rigging and other steel fittings, meters, etc they may be regarded as magnetic bearings, and after variation has been applied to them as shown above, the true bearings obtained can be drawn on the chart using the true rose. Suitable observing positions can be found for this compass by taking bearings of two visible charted objects when they are in line from several different positions in the cockpit. Those suitable are the positions from which the observed bearings agree with their correct magnetic bearings taken from the chart.

   In some large yachts the compass used for taking bearings is fixed to the cabin top or doghouse roof, and may in this position be subject subject to deviation. A deviation table must be provided for such a compass, and any bearings taken from it must be corrected in the manner described previously, before being laid off on the chart. It is essential to bear in mind that the deviation used for correcting a compass bearing must be that appropriate to the boat's heading at the time the bearing was taken.

Example: Assuming that the compass bearing of a light was 180° C with the boat heading 040° C, then if the deviation Table 5.2 was correct for this particular compass, the deviation to apply to the bearing would be 5° *Low* (that given for 040° C) and *not* 2° *High* (that given for 180° C). The magnetic bearing would therefore be 185° M.

Chapter 6

Laying a Course

The Track describes the path along which the boat has moved, or the path along which it is desired she should move. It often differs from the course because of the effects of wind and tidal streams.

LEEWAY Except when she is sailing with the wind astern, a sailing yacht, besides moving forwards, will be pushed sideways by the pressure of the wind on her sails, hull and gear. A power driven yacht will be similarly affected except when the wind is from ahead or from astern. This downwind movement, known as leeway, is expressed as an angle in degrees, and is the angle between the course that the yacht is steering, and the track that she is making good through the water. The amount of leeway made will depend on the yacht's draught, freeboard, speed, the strength and direction of the wind relative to her course, and the state of the sea. Yachts with shallow draught or high freeboard will make leeway more than those with deep draught or low freeboard, and a yacht closehauled will probably make more than one reaching. The amount can only be estimated, and this may be done by obtaining a magnetic bearing of the farthest visible part of the wake, or of the direction of the logline, reversing the bearing by adding

Fig. 6.1

or subtracting 180° and comparing the result with the boat's magnetic course. In power driven yachts and sailing yachts when reaching, any leeway made, once it has been estimated, can be counteracted by steering a course to windward of that obtained from the chart (Fig. 6.1).

Example: Track obtained from the chart 085° T, wind N (note: wind is named by direction *from* which it blows), estimated leeway 5°. The course to steer to make good 085° T is therefore 080° T (085° − 5°). Leeway cannot be allowed for in this way when a yacht is already sailing closehauled, and her track made good will therefore be to leeward of that steered. The amount made must be noted and then applied to leeward of the course steered when plotting the yacht's track on the chart.

Example: A yacht has steered a course of 100° T when closehauled, wind NE, estimated leeway 3°. Her track through the water is therefore 103° T (100° + 3°).

EFFECT OF CURRENT OR TIDAL STREAM When a stream is running directly with or against a yacht, her speed made good over the ground is equal to the sum of, or difference between, her speed through the water and the rate of the stream. If the stream is against a yacht, and its rate is more than her speed through the water, she will be carried backwards in the opposite direction to the course that she is steering. No allowance need be made when setting the course, but when from time to time the yacht's position has to be plotted on the chart, the distance that the stream has carried her forward or set her back, will have to be added to, or subtracted from, the distance sailed as shown by the log.

A stream setting obliquely across the yacht's course will carry her bodily in the direction that the stream is setting, and her track made good will be to one side or the other of her water track by an amount that depends on her speed through the water and the rate and direction of the stream. Because of the generally low speeds of yachts, this effect must always be considered before setting a course. Bearing in mind the distance to be covered and the yacht's probable speed through the water, the direct course should be steered if it appears, from the tidal stream atlas, that the effects of the stream will cancel out, or nearly cancel out, in the course of the passage, and there is plenty of sea room on either side of the direct line between the two places.

The yacht will be set to one side of the direct line, and then back, but the distance she will sail will be shorter than if she had continually counteracted the stream throughout the passage. Naturally it is rare that the effects of the stream exactly cancel out, but the practice should be to let as much as possible cancel out and then counteract for the rest of the passage. If, on the other hand, it appears that the stream will set generally in one direction throughout the passage, or if the proposed track takes the yacht close to some danger, then the tidal stream effect must be allowed for when setting the course.

To Find the Course to Steer (Water Track Angle) Allowing for the Tidal Stream

Assuming, for example, that a passage has to be made from a Lightvessel S to a buoy W off Calais, and that it is estimated that under the conditions existing at the time the yacht will sail at 5 knots through the water, what is the true course to steer for the first three hours allowing for the tidal stream?

The ground track to make is found by drawing a line on the chart between the lightvessel and the buoy, and the distance by measuring along this line with the dividers, using the latitude scale. In this example the track is found to be 130° T and the distance 15 miles.

The tidal stream tables on the chart for the lettered positions B, E and N are then examined, and from these it is estimated that the stream will set 227° T at 2·0 knots, 220° T at 2·7 knots, and 239° T at 1·5 knots, for the first, second and third hours respectively. The directions and the distances that the yacht would be carried by the stream if it experienced each prediction in turn for one hour are then laid off from the starting point S, using any convenient scale (see Fig. 6.2). The line SABC then represents the estimated total drift of the stream in three hours.

Then, having set the dividers or compasses, using the same scale, to the distance that the yacht is expected to sail in 3 hours (i.e. 15 units), place one leg at the end of the drift at C, and make a mark at F where the other leg cuts the ground track to make SW. Then C to F represents the water track angle from S , and if the parallel rulers are laid in this direction and then moved to the nearest rose, the true course (106° T) can be found, and by applying variation and deviation the compass course. The distance SF, to the same scale, represents the distance (13 miles) the yacht should make good in 3 hours.

Alternatively, when the stream is setting roughly in the same direction throughout, the directions and rates can be averaged in this

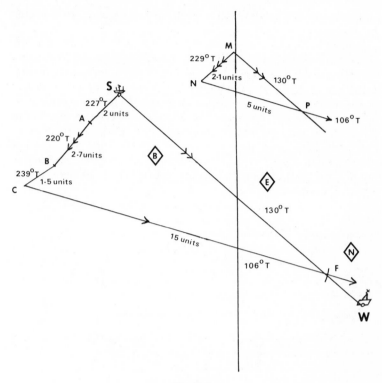

Fig. 6.2

example 229° T at 2 knots, and a triangle of velocities (MNP) drawn based on a time interval of 1 hour. MN then represents the average direction and rate of the stream, NP at water track angle (106° T) and MP the average speed the yacht should make good (4·3 knots).

The above construction, for finding the course to steer, can be done on any convenient part of the chart, as long as the lines which represent the track and the drift of the stream are drawn in their correct directions.

If, after the yacht has been set on her course, it is estimated that she is making leeway, then the course should be adjusted as described previously, so that she steers to windward of the water track.

The correctness of the course steered in the above example could be checked at first by taking back-bearings of the lightvessel while it remained visible, and laying them off on the chart. If the course is

83

correct, or nearly so, the bearings will very nearly coincide with the ground track.

It must be clearly understood that for the yacht to make good the required track, she must sail at the estimated speed used in the plot (in this case 5 knots), and the tidal stream must set exactly as predicted. In practice this is unlikely to occur, but the yacht should nearly make good her track as long as her speed is near that estimated. It may be, however, because of variations in the wind's strength and direction, or perhaps some mechanical fault in power driven craft, that after 2 hours on the course set in this example the yacht has logged only 8 miles instead of 10 miles. It will then be necessary to estimate the position, and find the new course to steer (water track) to the destination.

SUMMARY
Making Good an Intended Track

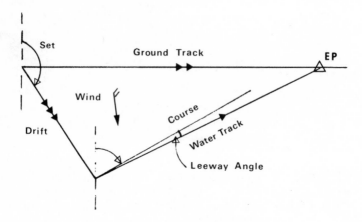

Fig. 6.3

Chapter 7

Plotting Positions

To Plot a Yacht's Estimated Position

The process of maintaining or predicting an approximate record of a boat's progress by projecting its course and distance from a known position is called 'dead reckoning'. A position obtained by dead reckoning, using true course steered and distance run by log, is a **DR position** (DR).

The best possible approximation of a present or future position is an **Estimated Position** (EP). It is based on course and distance since the last known position, with an estimation made for leeway, and for any set and drift of the tidal stream or current. Alternatively, the line of a series of earlier fixes produced can be used to estimate position.

The above terms are shown in Fig. 7.1 which illustrates the basic construction for DR and Estimated Positions.

Fig. 7.1

To Plot a Yacht's DR and Estimated Positions

Assume that the yacht in the previous example (Fig. 6.2) has logged 8 miles after sailing for two hours steering 101° T (107° M) to counter-act leeway estimated at 5° caused by a northerly wind, and that it is

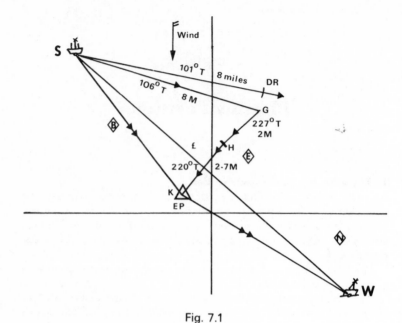

Fig. 7.1

required to plot her DR and Estimated positions with the tidal stream predictions for the first two hours as before, i.e. 227° T for 2 miles, and 220° T for 2·7 miles.

The DR position is first plotted by laying off from the lightvessel (S), the true or magnetic course steered using the True or the Magnetic rose. Then, having set the dividers to a distance of 8 miles on the latitude scale, place one leg of the dividers at S and make a mark where the other leg cuts the course line (Fig. 7.1). This point is the DR position and should be marked with a cross +, the log reading and time. This is the simplest and quickest position to plot, but probably the least accurate.

To then plot the yacht's estimated position (EP), first apply the leeway downwind of the course steered to find the *water track*. (If there is no leeway this step is missed out as the course steered becomes the water track.)

Course steered	101° T	(107° M)
Leeway	+5°	+5°
Water track	106° T	(112° M) Assuming variation is 6° W

Lay off the water track from S using the True (or Magnetic) rose, and then with the dividers set to a distance of 8 miles on the latitude scale, set one leg at S and mark the water track with the other leg at G (Fig. 7.1). The point G is called a **Sea Position**. Such a position takes account only of the boat's *motion through the water*.

From G now lay off the predicted directions and drifts of the stream for the first and second hours, i.e. 227° T for 2 miles (GH) and 220° T for 2·7 miles (HK). The end point K is the yacht's Estimated Position (EP) two hours after leaving the lightvessel. This point should have a small triangle drawn to enclose it, to indicate that it is an EP, and the log reading and time should be marked against it. The line SK is the **Ground Track** and represents the best estimation of the boat's motion over the ground. The line KW represents the new ground track to make good from K in order to reach buoy W.

A yacht's estimated position should be plotted in this way at regular intervals, whenever she is making a passage out of sight of land and her position cannot be fixed by bearings or other methods (see later text).

To Fix a Yacht's Position by Observation

While a yacht is making a passage along a coast, her position should be ascertained at regular intervals so that her navigator can see what track she is making good. In a sailing boat it is not essential that she keeps rigidly to the planned track, but it is important to know where she is from time to time. This is done when the yacht is close enough to the land by observing landmarks, and from these observations obtaining **position lines**.

A position line is any straight or curved line drawn on the chart on which the yacht's position is known to lie. The easiest way of obtaining a position line is by using the hand bearing compass to observe the bearing of a lighthouse (or a beacon, a lightvessel or other charted landmark), and then drawing a pencil line on the chart towards the charted position of the lighthouse in the same direction as the bearing.

Suppose, for example, that at 1530, the lighthouse L in Fig. 7.2 bears 060° M and variation is 10° W (*High*). The true bearing is then 050° T. If the parallel rules are laid across the nearest compass rose in the direction 050° T (060° M), and are then slid across the chart until one edge lies through L, then line PL drawn in the direction of 050° T (060° M) towards L is a position line. The yacht must lie somewhere on this line, because it runs through all the possible positions from which the lighthouse could bear 050° T. If at the same time the beacon

Fig. 7.2

B bears 003° M, which is 353° T, then a second position line BN can be drawn as before, and the yacht must also lie on this line for the same reason. The point of intersection of the two lines PL and BN, ringed with a small circle, is the only point from which these two bearings could have been observed, and therefore represents the yacht's position at 1530. Such a position is called a 'fix', and it should have marked beside it the time of observation and the log reading at that time, as shown in the figure.

A log reading is shown on the chart by marking the reading against a small triangle (e.g. in this case the reading is assumed to be 24). Another fix is shown for 1554 when the lighthouse and beacon were assumed to be bearing 005° M and 317° M respectively (355° T and 307° T respectively).

When a yacht's position is fixed by two bearings, the objects chosen should, if possible, be placed so that their bearings differ by nearly 90°, because the effect of any possible small errors in the taking or laying off of the bearings is thus decreased. If two position lines cut at an angle of less than 30° the fix should not be relied upon. Objects near the yacht should always be chosen in preference to objects far away.

Taking bearings requires practice. On some types the line across the compass, on the prism and the notch should all be in line as the bearing is taken. It will take time and probably require a mental average of readings at night, as a light may only show at 20 second intervals, and each time it appears the boat will have moved slightly.

Even on simpler compasses, the card swings and it has to be held level. (See Fig. 4.3A and D.)

When coasting a navigator should always be looking ahead for landmarks suitable for fixing his position. Quite often suitable landmarks, such as hills, islets, chimneys, churches, etc., are visible, but cannot be clearly identified on the chart. Such a landmark can usually be identified by fixing the yacht at least twice by means of known objects, and on each occasion simultaneously taking a bearing of the unknown object. If two or more such bearings are laid off from their respective fixes, the unidentified object will probably be found on the chart close to the point where the bearings intersect.

Example. In the previous example, a small island was seen to be bearing 079° M at 1530 and 070° M at 1554. When laid off from their respective fixes these two bearings (the dotted lines) cut close to Gull Island, and thus identified it.

On the same figure, the third fix at 1621 illustrates a transit, which is another method of obtaining a position line. If an observer sees two objects in line then he must be situated somewhere on the line joining them, produced in his direction. An excellent position line is obtained in this way, when the observer's distance from the nearer object is not more than about three times the distance between the objects. In this example, the centre of Gull Island was seen to be in line with Black Head at 1621 (as shown in Fig. 7.3) and the line TR represents the position line obtained. At the same time the lighthouse L bore 297° M, and this fixed the yacht's position when laid off on the chart.

Transit lines are often drawn on charts to act as clearing lines, as

Fig. 7.3

Fig. 7.4 Transit lines can be used as clearing lines, or as leading lines along which to steer, such as the two beacon transits used when entering the river. (Reproduced from the Cruising Association Handbook)

shown on the portion of chart in Fig. 7.4. They are ideal for use when the boat is being conned through a channel, particularly when the tidal stream is setting across the course. They enable quick adjustments to be made to the boat's course to keep her on the safe track without the necessity of a large number of bearings.

When a fix is obtained from bearings of three objects, their bearings should if possible differ by about 60° to give the best angle of cut. The three objects should either lie on, or nearly on, the same straight line, *or* the centre object should be nearer the yacht than a line joining the other two, *or* the yacht should lie within the triangle formed by lines joining the three objects.

When three bearings are taken the resulting position will not as a rule meet in a point; they will form a triangle known as a 'cocked hat'. If this is small, the position can usually be taken as its centre. If it is large, and a check has revealed no error in taking or laying off the bearings, the position should be taken as the corner of the cocked hat which will place the boat nearest to danger.

If there is any doubt about whether deviation is affecting the hand compass bearings, the boat's position can be fixed if three suitably placed charted objects (see above) can be seen, by observing the horizontal angles between pairs of objects in quick succession. The angles can be measured using the hand bearing compass in one chosen place in the cockpit with the boat on constant heading, or by using a sextant held horizontally, if one is carried in the boat. The method using the hand bearing compass is described here, as it can be used to check whether the hand bearing compass is being affected by deviation, and if so by how much.

Example. Assuming a yacht is in Mounts Bay and takes the following bearings using the hand bearing compass, which it is feared is being affected by her own magnetic field which is causing deviation. The yacht is steady on a course of 135° M.

A	Tater-du lighthouse	284° C
B	St Clements Island	322° C
C	St Michael's Mount Tower	016° C

It is required that the yacht's position is plotted using the method of horizontal angles, and that the hand bearing compass position is checked for deviation, assuming variation is 9° W.

The horizontal angles must be obtained first, by subtracting the first bearing from the second, and the second from the third.

B	St Clements Island	322° C
A	Tater-du lighthouse	−284° C
	Left hand angle	38°
C	St Michael's Mount Tr. 016° + 360°	= 376° C
B	St Clements Island	−322° C
	Right hand angle	54°

The terms 'left hand' and 'right hand' angles refer to the way the observer would see them.

1. Use a station pointer by setting the left hand and right hand movable arms to the above angles respectively; place the station pointer on the chart and move it about until the arms align themselves with the objects, and then mark the position at the centre of the station pointer (Fig. 7.5).

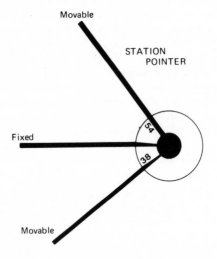

Fig. 7.5

2. Draw the bearing lines on tracing paper or a Douglas protractor at the observed angles, place on the chart and move about until the lines align themselves with the objects. Mark the chart at the intersection of the lines to give the position. (The Douglas protractor has a matt surface to enable lines to be drawn on it.) (Fig. 7.6.)

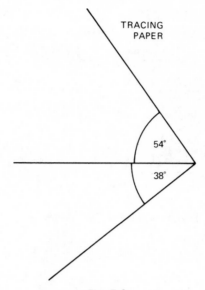

TRACING
PAPER

54°

38°

Fig. 7.6

3. Use tables in Reed's Nautical Almanac to obtain radii of the
    two position circles, and plot the circles to obtain the position.
    (See Reeds for details.)
4. Plot geometrically using a protractor and compasses to draw
    the intersecting position line circles.

The fourth method is described here in detail and shown in Fig. 7.7.

The position lines obtained from horizontal angles are two circles
passing through the left hand and right hand pairs of objects and the
yacht's position. In order to plot the position circles, the construction
must define the centre of each circle. The method is as follows:

1. Subtract each horizontal angle from 90° to obtain the 'base'
    angles of the 'centre' triangle. Here the base angles are:

    Left hand: $90° - 38° = 52°$

    Right hand: $90° - 54° = 36°$

2. Join the three objects by two straight lines, from A to B and
    from B to C, by pencil lines.
3. To construct the left hand circle, take a protractor and at A
    and B draw two lines from A and B, inclined to AB at the left
    hand base angle, to intersect at D. D is the centre of the left
    hand circle, of radius AD, which can now be drawn through A
    and B.

Reproduced from British Admiralty Chart No. 777 with the permission of the Controller of
H.M. Stationery Office and of the Hydrographer of the Navy

Fig. 7.7

4. Construct the right hand circle by the same method, by taking
    the protractor and at B and C drawing two lines from B and C,
    inclined to BC at the right hand base angles, to intersect at E.
    E is the centre of the right hand circle of radius BE. This can
    now be drawn through B and C, to cut the left hand circle in F
    which is the required position.

Note: The reasoning behind this construction involves the geometric
theorems which say that:

a. The three angles of a triangle sum to 180°; e.g. triangle ABD, so
    that the angle BDA equals 76°.
b. The angle at the centre of a circle is equal to twice the angle at the
    circumference standing on the same arc. (AB), e.g. angle
    BDA = 76° = 2 × angle BFA. Therefore angle BFA = 38° equals the
    observed left hand angle.
c. Angles in the same segment of a circle are equal. Therefore angle
    BFA, equal to 38°, would be obtained from any position on the

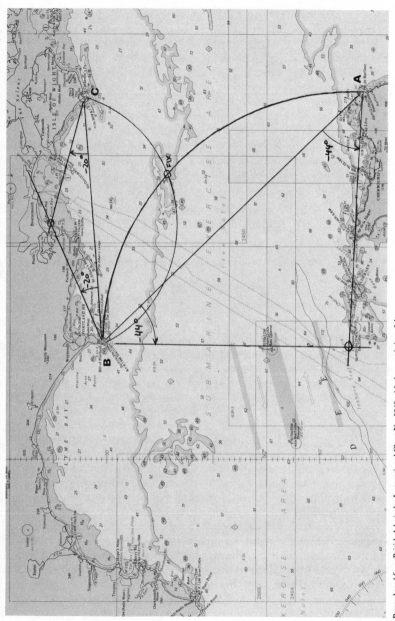

Fig. 7.8

95

circle ABF, and therefore satisfies the requirements of a position line.

From position F the true bearing of Tater-du is found to be 265° T and therefore the magnetic bearing is 265° T + 9° W (*High*) equal to 274° M. The compass bearing was 284° C and therefore that compass position is subject to deviation of 284° C − 274° M = 10° W (*High*) when on that particular course of 135° M.

If the yacht is inside the triangle formed by joining the three points A, B and C in Fig. 7.8, the angles observed between A and B, and B and C, will be greater than 90°. E.g. in Fig. 7.8 showing possible DF bearings of Cape Barfleur, Portland Bill and St Catherine's Point, the bearings were assumed to be:

A	Cape Barfleur	165° C
B	Portland Bill	299° C
C	St Catherine's Point	049° C

making the angles A to B 134°, and B to C 110°. To plot these angles as shown, follow the instructions as before, so that the base angles will be:

Left hand: 90° − 134° = − 44°
Right hand: 90° − 110° = − 20°

Take the above negative base angles as an indication that the yacht and the centre of each circle are on opposite sides of lines joining the places AB and BC. The only difference to the further instructions is to 3 and 4. These require, in 3 the base angle − 44° to be drawn to the westward of AB, and the base angle − 20° to be drawn on the land side of BC, to produce the two centres of the circles.

RISING AND DIPPING DISTANCES An approximate position line can be obtained at night when making a landfall, or when leaving the coast, by noting the time when a light with sufficient intensity first appears above the horizon, or dips below the horizon when going away from the light. The approximate distance from the light can then be calculated.

This distance is called the Geographical range, and is the maximum distance at which the light can theoretically reach an observer when limited only by the earth's curvature, normal atmospheric refraction, and by the elevation of the light and the observer's height of eye. The method should not be used therefore when there is abnormal refraction, which may be recognised by apparent mirage effects, or by raising the light at excessive range. The time at which the light appears or dips can be recognised if the observer changes the height at which he is keeping a lookout. The method is not an easy one to use in a yacht, because of its movement, and the range obtained should be regarded as approximate. The position line obtained in this way is a circle whose radius is equal to the yacht's distance from the light.

The range is obtained by adding the yacht's distance from the horizon to the distance of the light beyond the horizon (Fig. 7.9). These two distances can be found by entering a Distance of Sea Horizon table, or Geographical Range table, with the observer's height of eye above the sea, and the elevation of the light obtained from the chart, Light List or Almanac (Tables 7.1/2). Such a table is contained in all Light Lists and in Reed's Nautical Almanac. Because a light's charted height is given above MHWS, a distance obtained

Fig. 7.9

by using this height may be too small if the height of the tide at the time is much below MHWS. If maximum accuracy is required the estimated amount that the tide is below MHWS should be added to the charted height of the light before entering the table.

The power of a light must be considered before using this method, and it must not be used if the charted range is less than the range by calculation. When a light first appears above the horizon the yacht's movement in the seaway will increase and decrease the observer's height of eye (unless the sea is smooth) and may make the light's characteristic appear different from that charted. Before plotting the position line, time should be allowed for the yacht to move clearly within range of the light, so that its characteristic can be properly checked.

If a bearing is taken as soon as the light rises or dips, the yacht's position lies where the two position lines intersect (Fig. 7.10).

Fig. 7.10

Example. At 2216, log 49, when approaching Needles lighthouse from the south, its white light was raised bearing 002° T (009° M). The observer's height of eye was 1m (3ft) above the sea and the light's elevation was charted as 24m (80ft). Its charted Nominal range was 17 miles. Fix the yacht's position.

The Distance of the Sea Horizon table gives:

Distance of yacht from horizon (HE 3ft)	1·99 miles
Distance of light beyond horizon (Ht 80ft)	10·3 miles
Distance of yacht from light (approx.)	12·29 miles

As an alternative, entering the Geographical Range table with 1 metre in the top line and 24 metres down the side, gives the range as 12·0 miles (approximately).

DISTANCE OF SEA HORIZON
IN NAUTICAL MILES

Height in Feet	Distance in Miles	Height in Feet	Distance in Miles	Height in Feet	Distance in Miles	Height in Feet	Distance in Miles	Height in Feet	Distance in Miles
1	1·15	14	4·30	27	5·97	40	7·27	65	9·3
2	1·62	15	4·45	28	6·08	41	7·36	70	9·6
3	1·99	16	4·60	29	6·18	42	7·44	75	10·0
4	2·30	17	4·73	30	6·30	43	7·54	80	10·3
5	2·57	18	4·87	31	6·40	44	7·62	85	10·6
6	2·81	19	5·01	32	6·50	45	7·70	90	10·9
7	3·04	20	5·14	33	6·60	46	7·79	95	11·2
8	3·25	21	5·26	34	6·70	47	7·88	100	11·5
9	3·45	22	5·39	35	6·80	48	7·96	120	12·6
10	3·63	23	5·51	36	6·90	49	8·0	130	13·1
11	3·81	24	5·62	37	6·99	50	8·1	140	13·6
12	3·98	25	5·74	38	7·09	55	8·5	150	14·1
13	4·14	26	5·86	39	7·17	60	8·9	160	14·5

Table 7.1

If the geographical range exceeds the charted (nominal) range, the light is not powerful enough for this method to be used. The yacht's approximate position in this example is therefore 182° T, 12·0 miles from the Needles lighthouse.

THE RUNNING FIX The previous notes have described how a position can be fixed by making two observations at almost the same time. It will frequently be found, however, that when a fix is wanted only one suitable landmark is visible, and a bearing of this will only give one position line. Although a fix cannot be obtained at the time, the bearing should be taken and the position line laid off on the chart, because often this position line can be **transferred** and crossed with a second bearing taken later on of the same, or some other, landmark. A fix obtained in this way is known as a Running Fix. Its accuracy will mainly depend upon the accuracy of the estimated track and distance made good between the bearings and therefore this should be

Table 7.2

GEOGRAPHICAL RANGE TABLE

Elevation in		Height of Eye of Observer in feet/**metres**							
ft		3	7	10	13	16	20	23	26
	m	**1**	**2**	**3**	**4**	**5**	**6**	**7**	**8**
					Range in Sea Miles				
0	**0**	2·0	2·9	3·5	4·1	4·5	5·0	5·4	5·7
3	**1**	4·1	4·9	5·5	6·1	6·6	7·0	7·4	7·8
7	**2**	4·9	5·7	6·4	6·9	7·4	7·8	8·2	8·6
10	**3**	5·5	6·4	7·0	7·6	8·1	8·5	8·9	9·3
13	**4**	6·1	6·9	7·6	8·1	8·6	9·0	9·4	9·8
16	**5**	6·6	7·4	8·1	8·6	9·1	9·5	9·9	10·3
20	**6**	7·0	7·8	8·5	9·0	9·5	9·9	10·3	10·7
23	**7**	7·4	8·2	8·9	9·4	9·9	10·3	10·7	11·1
26	**8**	7·8	8·6	9·3	9·8	10·3	10·7	11·1	11·5
30	**9**	8·1	9·0	9·6	10·2	10·6	11·1	11·5	11·8
33	**10**	8·5	9·3	9·9	10·5	11·0	11·4	11·8	12·2
36	**11**	8·8	9·6	10·3	10·8	11·3	11·7	12·1	12·5
39	**12**	9·1	9·9	10·6	11·1	11·6	12·0	12·4	12·8
43	**13**	9·4	10·2	10·8	11·4	11·9	12·3	12·7	13·1
46	**14**	9·6	10·5	11·1	11·7	12·1	12·6	13·0	13·3
49	**15**	9·9	10·7	11·4	11·9	12·4	12·8	13·2	13·6
52	**16**	10·2	11·0	11·6	12·2	12·7	13·1	13·5	13·9
56	**17**	10·4	11·2	11·9	12·4	12·9	13·3	13·7	14·1
59	**18**	10·6	11·5	12·1	12·7	13·2	13·6	14·0	14·4
62	**19**	10·9	11·7	12·4	12·9	13·4	13·8	14·2	14·6
66	**20**	11·1	12·0	12·6	13·1	13·6	14·1	14·5	14·8
72	**22**	11·6	12·4	13·0	13·6	14·1	14·5	14·9	15·3
79	**24**	12·0	12·8	13·5	14·0	14·5	14·9	15·3	15·7
85	**26**	12·4	13·2	13·9	14·4	14·9	15·3	15·7	16·1
92	**28**	12·8	13·6	14·3	14·8	15·3	15·7	16·1	16·5

as short as possible, consistent with the requirement that the angle of cut should be as large as possible.

The method to be used in order to obtain a running fix can best be shown by means of an example.

Example. At 2145, the lighthouse L bore 320° M from a yacht steering 260° M. Log reading 24. Later, at 2230, log reading 27, the same lighthouse bore 040° M. From the chart, the tidal stream was estimated to be setting 230° T at 2 knots. Variation 10° W. Find the yacht's position at 2230.

Lay off the position lines PL and QL obtained from the bearings taken at 2145 and 2230 respectively. From any point A on the first

Fig. 7.11

position line, lay off the track made good through the water (allowing for leeway, if any) and the distance logged (AB = 3 miles) in the 45 minutes between the bearings. From B, lay off BC, which is the direction and distance (1·5 miles) the yacht is estimated to have been set by the tidal stream in 45 minutes. Then AC represents the estimated direction and distance made good over the ground between the bearings. Through C draw the line SYCR parallel to the first position line. The yacht's estimated position, 45 minutes after taking the first bearing, must lie somewhere on this line, which is known as a transferred position line, and is usually distinguished by two arrowheads at each end. The point Y, where the transferred position line cuts the second position line QL, is the yacht's position at 2230 (Fig. 7.11).

USING A SINGLE POSITION LINE At times, when coasting or making the land in moderate visibility, it is only possible to obtain one position line. When this line lies in a suitable direction, it may often be used to clear some danger or to make the entrance to a harbour.

Suppose, for example, that a yacht is making for harbour H in Fig. 7.12 and is approaching the coast in moderate and decreasing visibility after a passage of about 50 miles since the last fix. At 0300, log reading 61, the powerful flashing light B is sighted bearing 200° M, obviously well within its maximum range, and that this bearing when drawn on the chart gives a position line which lies some miles to the E of the yacht's estimated position.

Although the yacht's most likely position on the position line is the point marked A nearest to her estimated position, her navigator cannot be sure of his distance from the light. Because of this and the decreasing visibility, he cannot safely alter course from A direct for the harbour and assume that he will get a second bearing and hence a running fix, as he may not see the light again.

His safest plan, in these circumstances, is to assume that he is closer to the light than he thinks he is, for example at point D, and then to alter to a course (DE) which, bearing in mind the possible effect of the tidal stream, takes the yacht parallel to or if necessary away from, the

Fig. 7.12

coast. He should then transfer his position line (HC) through the harbour entrance, or fairway buoy, and carefully plot his estimated position at intervals as he steers his new course. As soon as he estimates that he has reached the transferred position line (i.e. at F), he should alter course again and steer a course that makes good the direction of the position line (i.e. 200° M), counteracting the tidal stream as necessary (Fig. 7.12).

He can then approach the harbour in reasonable safety, knowing the direction in which it lies, until the occulting light at the entrance is seen. If the visibility is poor during the final approach occasional soundings should be taken; and if the light has not been seen by the time the soundings have decreased to say 6 fathoms in this example, the yacht should be turned about onto the opposite course, or anchored, until the visibility has improved. The limiting sounding must be governed by the nature of the particular coastline: for steep, rocky coastlines, the 20 metre (10 fathoms) line should be the limit; for shelving coastlines, the 10 metre (6 fathoms) line.

LINE OF SOUNDINGS It is sometimes necessary to make a landfall and an approach to a position in conditions of poor visibility or fog. If possible, some thought should be given to this and preparations made to assist in making the approach safely, so that the yacht's position is known with reasonable certainty. Assuming that radar is not carried and that radio direction finding is not usable in the particular area concerned, it will mean that soundings (preferably with an echo sounder) and fog signals will have to be used. If the approach is to be made to a position off a lighthouse which operates a fog signal, or to a harbour entrance, the destination position must be chosen so that there is a reasonable chance of hearing the fog signal. The position must not be too far from the lighthouse. At the same time, it must be possible to check by soundings whether a wrong approach is being made, in case the fog signal is not heard. Remember that sound signals in fog are notoriously uncertain (see Chapter 2) but may be all that is available. Some limit must be put on the approach, either distance run or minimum depth, so that if the position is not made and positively identified the boat can be anchored, stopped or turned round, to await improved visibility.

An example may help to show how a **line of soundings** may be used to decide one's position in thick fog. It must be borne in mind that in any such approach some allowance must be made for the height of tide, if soundings are to be used to fix the position. Before a sounding is compared with the soundings on the chart, the approximate height of tide must be subtracted to 'reduce' the sounding to chart datum. This process is known as 'Reduction to Soundings'.

In the example which is considered now, of a yacht making for a position 1 mile south of St Anthony Head in the approaches to Falmouth in thick fog, having started from a position 2 miles south of Eddystone lighthouse some 27 miles to the eastward, there would probably have been sufficient time to have estimated the height of tide in the Falmouth approaches using the method shown in Chapter 3. For example, if the approach had been made on the afternoon of 8 August (BST), the height of tide would have been approximately 3m at 1500, 4m at 1600, 4·7m at 1700 and 5m at HW around 1800. (Based on HW Falmouth at 1806 BST, height 5·2m, duration of rise 5h 56 min; LW at 1210, 0·7m.) This would mean, if the yacht was crossing

104

Fig. 7.13

Fig. 7.14

the 50m contour line of the chart at about 1600, that the actual sounding when this occurred would be 54m (29½ fathoms), and the time should be noted when 54m (29½ fathoms) is observed on the sounder (Fig. 7.13).

It is assumed that the approach is being made on auxiliary engine at 3 knots over the ground and steering to make good a track of 268° T while listening for the fog signal which is a horn. In this discussion the 30m line has been disregarded to avoid complication.

If the attempted approach line is B, and soundings are observed, the following might be the possible pattern of corrected soundings and times recorded along the different marked approach lines shown in Fig. 7.13. Time intervals are in minutes between the respective contour lines (Fig. 7.14).

The 10m line has been taken as the absolute limit line to turn on or anchor.

If A was the approach line, the fog signal may not be heard because of the land intervening, but if he heard it should appear to come from ahead. The 5 minute interval when the soundings decreased from 20m and then increased again to 20m is fairly distinctive. Decisions may have to be made fairly early in an approach such as this. If the dividers are set to the distance observed between say the 50m and 20m contour, i.e. 27 mins at 3 knots is 1·4 miles, and are then moved over the chart parallel to the track, it may be possible to estimate the probable track after one line has been crossed. A better indication may be given after a further line has been timed. The lines shown above show that in this area each line of soundings is probably unique, and could be used to fit to the chart to obtain a line of position.

If B was being made good, it is possible the horn fog signal would be heard apparently about 45° on the starboard bow as the 20m line was approached. If so the signal would gradually broaden on the bow, until when the 20m line is crossed again it would be heard apparently on the starboard beam after about 21 minutes. The pattern for D is very similar as it is only half a mile south of B.

If the yacht had been set to the south, on tracks C or E, the soundings would decrease continuously in a fairly distinctive way, but the fog signal might not be heard.

The situation might develop as follows. With the soundings indicating that the yacht is probably making good track D, it could be envisaged, having heard the fog signal gradually broaden on the starboard bow until it is at last apparently abeam, with sounding at

Reproduced from British Admiralty Instructional Chart No. 5066 with the permission of the Controller of H.M. Stationery Office and of the Hydrographer of the Navy.

Fig. 7.15

20m for the second time, that course could be altered to about 345° T to put the fog signal a few degrees on the starboard bow again, so that a closer approach could be made in order to sight the lighthouse if possible. If nothing is sighted by the time the 10m contour is reached, the yacht should be anchored to await improved visibility. If the yacht is apparently to the southward on tracks C or E, on reaching the 10m line she should be either stopped or anchored. From there it may be possible to follow the 10m line to the north until something is sighted and identified, or the yacht is anchored closer to the entrance in 10m. If there are doubts at any time, stop, anchor if possible, or turn and retrace the track for a bit.

A more positive position line is obtained by taking a line of soundings when the yacht crosses a clearly defined shallow ridge or deeper trough in the seabed, as shown on the chart of the approaches to Le Touquet (Fig. 7.15). This should not be done in a blow, as there may be heavy breaking seas. The crossing of the ridge enclosed by the 6 fathom line (– – – – – –) with soundings of 3 to 4 fathoms gives a clear position line with an accuracy of about 4 cables. The later crossing, about 1 mile further on, of the 10 fathom line (· — · — · — · — · — · — ·) again is a clear position line giving an indication of how many miles to go in poor visibility. It might be used in conjunction with the lighthouse or light in moderate visibility to fix position.

The pattern of soundings has got to be suitable for a line of soundings to be used in this way, and generally the contour lines should be continuous, with no areas marked with no soundings, which would indicate a poor and incomplete survey.

Radio Aids to Navigation

RADIOBEACONS Marine radiobeacons are generally radio transmitters which transmit easily identifiable signals in all directions, so that a vessel fitted with direction finding apparatus can fix its position in fog, or when other suitable landmarks are too far off to be visible.

The abbreviation Ro. Bn. in black, or RC in magenta, plus a magenta circle in each case, indicates on charts the lighthouses and lightvessels equipped with radiobeacons.

Many beacons provide a continuous service by transmitting their characteristic signals for one minute at regular specified intervals, day and night, in fog and in clear weather; other beacons transmit only in fog and make no clear weather transmissions.

All marine radiobeacons situated on the coasts of Europe and the British Isles transmit on frequencies between 285 and 315 kHz (1053 and 952 metres), and the form of the characteristic signals transmitted by those north of Lat. 46° N has been standardised as follows:

1.	The identification signal transmitted 3 to 6 times for approx.	22 sec
2.	A long dash lasting for	25 sec
3.	The identification signal transmitted once or twice for approx.	8 sec
4.	A silent period of at least	5 sec
	Total	60 sec

A prolonged silent period usually follows. A beacon's identification signal usually consists of two letters related to its name and transmitted in Morse code.

To make it easier to obtain a fix in some areas, certain beacons have been linked in rotation in groups of 2, 3 or 6 beacons which transmit one at a time on the same frequency. This allows at least two bearings of different beacons to be obtained without retuning the receiver.

Certain aircraft radiobeacons (aerobeacons) are situated near the coast, and they may often be used to obtain bearings when other beacons are not suitable. However, they should be used with caution because of possible coastal refraction (see later note). Their characteristic signals usually consist of a two or three letter identification signal in Morse, followed by a long dash, and they usually operate continuously between stated times.

The ranges, signals, frequencies and transmission times of beacons in European waters are contained in the Admiralty List of Radio Signals and nautical almanacs.

THE PRINCIPLE OF THE DIRECTION FINDER is based on the directive properties of a plane vertical loop aerial, or alternatively a horizontal ferrite rod aerial. The strength of the signal heard depends upon the angle between the vertical plane through the aerial and the direction of the beacon. As the aerial is slowly rotated, so the signal strength varies from a maximum to zero. The rate of change of signal strength is greatest near the zero positions, and therefore the bearing pointer is fixed to the aerial so that the direction of the incoming radio waves is indicated when the signal strength is zero. This occurs when the plane of a loop aerial is at right angles to, or when a rod aerial is in line with, the direction of the beacon. Two zero positions, approximately 180° apart, will be observed if the rod or loop is rotated through 360°, and therefore an approximate bearing of each beacon must be obtained from the yacht's estimated position on the chart in order to decide which one is correct.

The zero or null position is either obtained aurally by using the earphones, or visually by means of a signal strength meter. A sense-finding circuit included in some receivers can be used to resolve the 180° ambiguity mentioned above.

DF PROCEDURE Bearings obtained with the fixed type of set are relative to the boat's fore-and-aft line, expressed in three figures where 000° indicates ahead, 090° indicates the starboard beam, 180° indicates astern, and 270° indicates the port beam (Fig. 7.16). This type of set should be fixed if possible in line with the keel and as far away from the mast and rigging as possible. The 0°–180° line on the bearing plate should be in, or parallel to, the boat's fore-and-aft line. In steel yachts bearings will have to be taken from a position on deck.

After the yacht's estimated position has been marked on a small scale chart, the two (three if possible) nearest beacons which will give a reasonable angle of cut should be chosen, and their approximate bearings relative to the yacht's heading obtained from the chart. The frequencies, identification signals and transmission times are then looked up and the set tuned to the frequency of the first beacon to transmit. If the beacons are grouped, the set will not require retuning.

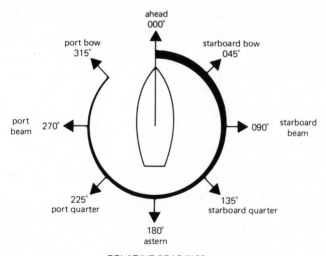

RELATIVE BEARINGS

Fig. 7.16

Each bearing is taken in the following manner, after disconnecting the vertical aerial (if any) and plugging in the earphones.

The aerial loop or rod is rotated until the bearing pointer is roughly at right angles to the beacon's direction obtained from the chart, so that as soon as the beacon transmits its signal will be heard at maximum strength.

After the beacon has been heard and identified, and as soon as the long continuous note commences, the loop or rod should be rotated until the signal is no longer heard. The aerial should then be swung slightly to each side of this direction in order to decide the exact zero (null) position. As soon as this is achieved the bearing and the exact compass heading of the boat should be noted at the same instant, together with the time and log reading. The bearings for the chart are then obtained by adding the corrected DF bearings (see later note on quadrantal error) to the boat's true or magnetic headings respectively.

Such a fixed type of DF set will be more usually found in larger yachts or fishing vessels. It has been largely superseded by the hand-held instrument which incorporates a ferrite rod aerial and a bearing compass, as shown in Figs. 4.9, 4.10.

When taking bearings with this type the receiver and rod aerial must be tuned to the frequency of the beacon, which must be identified with the rod aerial approximately at right angles to the direction of the beacon (i.e. the maximum signal position). On hearing the long dash, the instrument must be rotated until the signal is zero and then oscillated slightly each side of this position until it is clearly identified. The bearing is then read from vertically above the card, or by facing the direction of the beacon and viewing the bearing in the prism. Bearings obtained in this way may have to be corrected for quadrantal error and for compass deviation before plotting them on the chart. Errors due to yawing of the boat should be reduced by using this type of instrument. Where the aerial, compass and the receiver are in one unit, the batteries should be checked before fitting to see if they cause any compass deviation. They may require de-magnetising.

Example. The following DF bearings were obtained when approaching the French coast, using fixed DF equipment:

At 1303, Roches Douvres radiobeacon bore 296° relative, quadrantal error −1°, with the yacht heading 169° C. At 1304, Île-Vierge radiobeacon bore 048° relative, quadrantal error +4°, with the yacht heading 172° C. Deviation 1° W (*High*), variation 8° W (*High*), log reading 73. What are the true bearings to lay off on the chart? (Fig. 7.17)

Reproduced from British Admiralty Instructional Chart No. 5053 with the permission of
the Controller of H.M. Stationery Office and the Hydrographer of the Navy.

Fig. 7.17

	Roches Douvres				*Île-Vierge*		
Comp. C.	169°C	DF brg.	296°	Comp. Co.	172°C	DF brg	048°
Dev.	−1°H	Quad. err.	−1°	Dev.	−1°H	Quad. err.	+4°
Mag. Co.	168°M	Rel. brg.	295°	Mag. Co.	171°M	Rel. brg.	052°
Var.	−8°H	True Co.	+160°T	Var.	−8°H	True Co.	+163°T
True Co.	160°T		455°	True Co.	163°T	True brg.	215°T
			−360°				
		True Brg.	095°T				

If the bearings had been taken on the above yacht using a hand-held DF instrument, assumed to be unaffected by compass deviation, the observations might have been recorded as:

At 1303 with course approximately 170° C, deviation 1° W (*High*), Roches Douvres radiobeacon bore 104° M and at 1304 Île-Vierge radiobeacon bore 219° M. Variation 8° W (*High*). What are the true bearings if the quadrantal error curve shows −1° and +4° for relative bearings of 295° Rel. and 050° Rel.?

Compass Co. 170° C − 1° W (*High*) = Magnetic Co. 169° M.

	Roches Douvres				*Île-Vierge*		
Mag. brg.	104° M	DF Mag. brg.	104° M	Mag. brg.	219° M	DF Mag. brg.	219° M
	+360°	Quad. err.	−1°	Mag. Co.	−169° M	Quad. err.	+4°
	464°	Mag. brg.	103° M	Rel. brg. for			
Mag. Co.	−169° M	Var.	−8° H	Quad. err.	050°	Mag. brg.	223° M
Rel. brg. for				Quad. err.	+4°	Var.	−8° H
Quad. err.	295°	True brg.	095° T			True brg.	215° T
Quad. err.	−1°						

Note: If there is no quadrantal error curve, there is no need to work out the relative bearing for each observation. The variation is applied to the bearing to get the true bearing. This is quicker and easier, but might be less accurate.

If a small 'cocked hat' results from bearings of three well-placed beacons, considerable reliance may be placed on the fix. If the cocked hat is large the observations should be repeated if possible; if this is not possible, the fix should be regarded as unreliable. Practice DF bearings should be taken whenever possible, particularly when the resulting fixes can be checked by visual bearings, as a navigator can thereby judge the accuracy of his radio bearings. This will help him to decide how much reliance he can place on a fix when only radio bearings are available.

DF bearings are not the be-all and end-all of navigation because they are quite difficult to take accurately and are subject to errors. They should be regarded as aids to navigation to be used with all the other information available.

Errors

NIGHT EFFECT During the period from one hour before sunset to one hour after sunrise, signals from beacons more than 25 miles distant may be received via the ionosphere (sky waves) as well as parallel to the earth's surface (ground waves). The reception of sky waves may cause the signals to fade, or give blurred and indefinite nulls, and bearings which are obtained by using such signals are liable to be incorrect. During the above period, therefore, DF bearings should only be taken of beacons which are less than 25 miles away.

COASTAL REFRACTION (LAND EFFECT) Ground waves from a beacon situated some distance inland may be deflected towards the coastline by as much as 5° if they cross the coast at an oblique angle as they pass from land to sea. Waves travelling parallel to a coastline may be deflected either away from or towards it. When this occurs the bearing obtained will not indicate the direction of the beacon. To avoid this error always use marine beacons if possible; and if an aircraft beacon has to be used, choose one where the path of the wave from beacon to vessel crosses the coastline nearly at right angles.

QUADRANTAL ERROR This error is caused by magnetic fields of the vessel's hull, rigging and mast, which sometimes deflect radio waves so that incorrect bearings are obtained. If possible, the lower ends of shrouds and stays should be insulated from their rigging screws and chainplates. Plastic tubing or a good marline service over the wire where it passes round the thimble is satisfactory. If this is carried out errors in wooden vessels will probably be negligible, but in steel vessels may still be appreciable.

In order to detect these errors, DF and visual relative bearings should be taken at headings every 10° or 20° all round the vessel, by steadying her on many different courses when she is 3 to 5 miles from a radiobeacon. At least two people will be required, one to take the DF bearings, and the other to steer, note the heading and take bearings with the hand bearing compass at the same time as the DF bearings are taken. Table 7.3 will give some idea of what is required.

Table 7.3

A	B	C	D	E	F	G
Ship's Head by Steering Compass	Steering Compass Deviation (if any)	Magnetic Heading $(A \pm B)$	Magnetic Bearing of Beacon by Hand Bearing Compass	Relative Bearing $(D - C)$	DF Bearing (Relative)	Error $(E - F)$
080° C	5° LOW	085° M	128° M	043°	039°	+4°
062° C	5° LOW	067° M	132° M	065°	062°	+3°
052° C	5° LOW	057° M	140° M	083°	081°	+2°
			and so on			

The vessel is steadied on a suitable course, and then one person takes a DF bearing of the beacon (column F). The other person immediately notes the ship's head (column A), then takes and notes the bearing of the beacon with the hand bearing compass (column D). The procedure is carried out on a succession of courses so that the relative bearing changes by about 20° between each bearing. The remaining columns are completed after all the bearings have been taken. Column E is completed by subtracting C from D, after adding 360° to D if necessary. The errors are obtained by subtracting F from E. If the bearing in F is greater than that in E, the error is negative. Note that the sign of the error indicates how it should be applied to a DF bearing in order to obtain the correct relative bearing.

If the hand-held type of DF instrument is checked for quadrantal error, the columns in the table should be drawn up as shown below after one person has noted the boat's heading by compass, and the other has taken the DF bearing and then the visual bearing with the same instrument (Table 7.4)

Table 7.4

A	B	C	D	E	F	G
Boat's Head by Steering Compass	Steering Compass Deviation (if any)	Magnetic Heading (A ± B)	Visual Magnetic Bearing of Beacon by hand bearing compass	DF Magnetic Bearing of Beacon by hand held instrument	Relative DF Bearing (E − C)	Error (D − E)
080° C	5° LOW	085° M	128° M	124° M	039°	+ 4°

and so on

It is assumed in columns D and E that the compass used has no deviation at the positions from which the bearings were taken. The errors should either be tabulated against DF bearings or a curve drawn with plus errors marked above and minus errors marked below a horizontal axis indicating DF bearings and marked from 0° to 360°.

CONSOL Consol is a long-range navigational radio aid primarily intended for aircraft. It can be used by vessels equipped with a suitable medium frequency receiver. Consol signals can be received on any of the radio sets designed and sold for use in yachts.

A Consol beacon is an automatic radio transmitter with a special directional aerial system. The radiation pattern from each beacon consists of alternate sectors of dot and dash signals, separated by equisignals (heard faintly as a short, steady note). Each sector is approximately 15° wide, and the radiation pattern on one side of the line of the aerials is the mirror image of the pattern on the other side

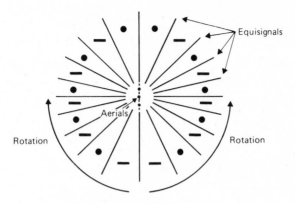

Fig. 7.18   Radiation Pattern of Consol Beacon

(see Fig. 7.18). During each transmission cycle, the two halves of the pattern rotate uniformly in opposite directions until each equisignal has moved through one sector's width. The rotation then ceases and the pattern reverts to its original position ready for the next cycle. During this short time the beacon's identification signal (2 or 3 letters in Morse) and a long dash are transmitted. An observer will therefore hear an equisignal once in each cycle, and his angular position in a sector is determined by the number of dot or dash characters heard before the equisignal.

METHOD OF USE Tune the receiver to the frequency of the beacon, and correctly identify it by listening for the identification signal. Where possible a vertical aerial should be used, but a DF set may be used as long as the loop is not turned away more than 45° either side of its position for maximum signal strength. The total number of dots and dashes heard is then counted by the observer. If he is in a dot sector he will hear dots, equisignal and then dashes; in a dash sector he will hear dashes, equisignal and then dots. The total number of dots and dashes heard should add up to 60, but in practice some of the characters are lost because they appear to merge in the equisignal at the change from one symbol to the other. The actual count is therefore corrected to allow for the lost characters by subtracting the total observed count from 60, and adding half the difference to the dot count and half to the dash count.

For example: Observed count 40 dashes – equisignal – 16 dots.
Total count 56. Difference $60 - 56 = 4$, Half diff. $= 2$.
Corrected count 42 dashes – equisignal – 18 dots.

Fig. 7.19   A Consol Fix

A position line is obtained by applying the average of several counts of the characters heard *before* the equisignal to a Consol chart, which has position lines printed on it at 5 or 10 character intervals. The position lines appropriate to each beacon are marked in different colours.

A corrected count will give a position line in each of several sectors, so that the vessel's estimated position must be plotted on the Consol chart to decide which is the correct sector. The exact position line can then be easily interpolated by eye in the vicinity of the estimated position.

The vessel's position can be fixed by taking a DF bearing of a radiobeacon and thus obtaining a second position line.

COVERAGE is about 140° on either side of the aerial baseline at each beacon. The Stavanger (Norway) beacon provides position lines over most of the North Sea, and the Plonéis (NW France) beacon covers the Western Approaches to the British Isles, south of Ireland. A position line cannot be obtained when within 25 miles of a Consol beacon. The system is not considered sufficiently accurate for making a precise landfall, but is a useful aid in open waters.

Example. During a passage from Falmouth to Cork in DR position 51° 04′ N, 7° 12′ W, the following Consol counts were obtained:

    Plonéis   24 dashes – equisignal – 30 dots
    Stavanger 12 dots   – equisignal – 40 dashes
Determine the yacht's position (see Fig. 7.19).
    The corrected counts are:
    Plonéis   27 dashes – equisignal – 33 dots
    Stavanger 16 dots   – equisignal – 44 dashes
The 27-dash position line for Plonéis and the 16-dot line for Stavanger are marked in Fig. 7.19. The yacht's position was 50° 58′ N, 7° 12′ W.

VHF RADIO LIGHTHOUSES transmit on Channel 88 (162·025 MHz) directional signals which reach approximately horizon range to seaward. Range is largely governed by transmitter height but on average is 20 miles. The directional signal consists of a minimum or null in the radio signal which is made to rotate electronically over a 120° sector at a constant rate. *The system is still experimental, however, and the following may be subject to change.*

On an ordinary VHF receiver, the user hears a Morse identifier and then a tone which decreases in loudness until the null radial passes through his position, after which it gets louder. The tone is broken up into timing pips or beats, two per second, which are counted until the null is reached; beats 10, 20, 30, 40, 50 and 60 are emphasised by a change in pitch. The full transmission cycle takes 60 seconds. The count of beats heard before the null is entered in a table to obtain the bearing of the radio lighthouse from seaward, to an accuracy of 2°. The accuracy of bearings is unaffected by the boat's movement and independent of her heading. VHF radio lighthouses are planned to operate in alternation in pairs; a count of the beats from a second one within range provides a second bearing and a fix when crossed with the first bearing. (Tables are in Admiralty List of Radio Services for Small Craft.)

Chapter 8

Passage Making

PLANNING A PASSAGE The charts and pilot books required for the passage should be obtained some time before the proposed departure, so that they can be studied at leisure and a plan prepared before sailing. They should include charts for harbours and coasts which lie near the waters in which the passage is to be made, in case the plan has to be altered because of bad weather or other causes.

The track to be followed should be drawn on a small scale chart which shows both the point of departure and the destination. It can then be redrawn on the large scale charts which will be used while making the passage.

The track should be drawn close enough to the shore to make certain that all lighthouses and beacons can be seen so that frequent fixes can be obtained. As a guide, when the coast is steep-to aim to pass it at a distance of about 2 miles; when the coast is shelving, yachts drawing less than 3m (10ft) should pass outside the 5m (3 fathom) line. Overfalls or races should be avoided. Where there are unmarked dangers out of sight of land, aim to pass them at a distance of at least 5 miles, and at night this distance should be increased.

Departure should be timed to give the longest possible period with a fair stream during the passage. The most suitable time can be worked out by marking each page in the tidal stream atlas with the actual times appropriate for the chosen day of sailing and the following day, and then from various assumed starting times running through the passage at the boat's estimated speed, increasing or decreasing it as necessary to allow for the probable tidal stream effect. When considering departure times, other factors which may decide the best time should be borne in mind. For instance, it may be necessary to arrive at a certain position at slack water, or at a harbour entrance at daybreak; after a passage partly out of sight of land, it is often easier to make a landfall just before dawn when lights are still visible. In these cases, it is better to work back from the required position and time in order to find the departure time. When finally deciding a suitable time, some allowance should always be made for unforeseen wind shifts etc., and for the fact that a vessel nearly always tends to be late at a position rather than early.

Finally, before sailing, a weather forecast should be obtained through one of the BBC broadcasts, or by telephone to one of the Meteorological Offices. Weather broadcasts and other services are in nautical almanacs and List of Radio Services for Small Craft.

Yachtsmen keeping their boats or making coastal passages in UK waters are strongly advised to contact the local HM Coastguard station and join the Yacht and Boat Safety Scheme. By completing form CG66 a boat's owner provides the Coastguard with full particulars of his boat's appearance and equipment should search and rescue action be needed. The same information should be left with a responsible person ashore.

MAKING A PASSAGE After leaving her berth, a yacht will usually have to be navigated by buoys, beacons or leading lines until she reaches the sea. This should not present any difficulty in clear weather if the chart has been studied before leaving. When leaving (or entering) harbours with narrow entrances, a careful watch should be kept for harbour traffic signals, which are displayed to stop vessels leaving when another is entering, or vice versa.

Such signals are described in the pilot book for the area and many are given in nautical almanacs. They must be obeyed. After passing the harbour or river entrance, it may still be necessary to navigate for some miles along one of a number of different channels between sandbanks before the departure point for the passage is reached (e.g. Thames Estuary). In these circumstances, the name or number of each buoy to be passed, together with the magnetic or compass course from each buoy to the next, should be written in a notebook so that it can be referred to whenever the direction of the next buoy is not known with certainty. This would be of great assistance in poor visibility and near areas where two or more channels combine, as it is very easy to steer for the wrong buoy unless this precaution is taken. On a rising tide sandbanks may often be crossed with safety in fine weather after the tide has risen sufficiently to give a good clearance under the keel, but no risk should be taken on a falling tide as if the yacht grounds she would be unlikely to refloat for several hours.

The log should be streamed or switched on before reaching the end of the approach channel, and as soon as the last buoy is passed the yacht should be put on her first course, counteracting the tidal stream if necessary. The log should then be set to zero, or its reading noted, and together with the time, written on the chart alongside the buoy. Her position should then be fixed at regular intervals by cross bearings, while suitable landmarks are visible. When making a passage out of sight of land, the yacht's estimated position should be plotted at regular intervals as convenien... If a radio direction-finder is carried the estimated positions can occasionally be checked and adjusted by taking DF bearings.

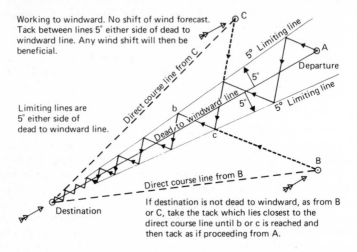

Fig. 8.1

A sailing yacht will often find that her destination or the position off the next headland, lies dead to windward, and she will then have to tack each side of her direct course. In these circumstances it will not pay her to deviate too far from the direct course line, unless a shift of wind is forecast, or perhaps a favourable tidal stream or smoother water will be experienced. A good plan is to keep her tacking within two lines drawn about 5° on either side of the direct course line as shown in Fig. 8.1. If a shift of wind is forecast these two lines should be drawn on the same side of the direct course line as the wind is expected to shift (Fig. 8.2). If a tidal stream has also to be considered when working to windward, a yacht should be kept for as long as possible on the tack that makes the least angle with the direction of a foul tidal stream; on the other hand she should be kept on the tack that makes the largest angle with the direction of a fair tidal stream.

Working to windward with a forecast wind shift to the right. (veer)
Tack between dead to windward line and a line 10° away on the side towards which the wind is expected to shift.

Forecast wind direction

If wind shifts to here when yacht has reached d, she can lay her destination direct.

Destination

C

10° Limiting line

Departure
A

Direct course line from C

Dead to windward line

b

10°

d
c

B

Direct course line from B

From departure positions B or C, proceed as in previous figure.

Fig. 8.2

If fog or mist sets in during a passage, lifejackets should be put on and a fog signal made at intervals of not more than one minute, preferably with a foghorn. If the practice of regularly fixing the yacht's position has been followed, there will be a recent fix on the chart which can be used to estimate her present position and decide future action. A yacht situated in a busy shipping lane is in a dangerous position, as small craft are not easily detected on other vessels' radar screens, and her fog signal is usually low powered. A yacht may sometimes be detected on a radar screen at a greater range if a metal radar reflector is hoisted to the masthead, but this should not be relied upon to indicate the yacht's presence because radar is not carried by all vessels. Probably the best action is to work clear of the shipping lane into less frequented waters. If the coast is near and shelving, she can then stand in towards the shore, taking frequent soundings, until the water is shallow enough to anchor; off a rocky steep coastline, she should be kept well clear.

If it is decided to continue the passage, the navigator will have to make use of all the aids at his disposal to keep a check on his yacht's position. These include a good lookout, soundings, fog signals from lighthouses, lightvessels and buoys, and DF bearings. He must also carefully plot his estimated position at regular intervals. Many light-houses and lightvessels indicate their positions by making character-istic air fog signals at regular intervals (see page 18).

Fog signals are heard at greatly varying distances and on occasions may be inaudible, even when close, because of the prevailing air conditions. They must always be approached with caution, and other means of finding the yacht's position must not be neglected.

When navigating along a coast from one fog signal to another the course steered should allow for any tidal stream effect, so as to make good a track which lies roughly parallel to the coastline and passes close enough to the fog signal for it to be heard. Check soundings should be taken, and sometimes where the charted soundings are closely spaced and regular a contour line may be followed until the fog signal is heard.

If the yacht is coming from the sea to try to hear a fog signal, it is not normally advisable to steer straight for it. Her navigator should steer for a point on a suitable contour line several miles to one side of the fog signal, so that when his soundings tell him that he has reached this contour line, he will know with some certainty on which side the fog signal lies. He can then alter course parallel to the coast and follow the contour towards the fog signal.

ARRIVING AT THE DESTINATION The Pilot should be read and the chart examined before entering so that the navigator has a picture of the place in his mind. If the destination is an anchorage, the height of tide must be known so that the yacht can be anchored in sufficient depth of water to ensure that she remains afloat at low water. The Pilot will usually describe suitable anchorages, and the best approach to them. As soon as the yacht is anchored, the depth of water should be checked with the lead, and anchor bearings taken. These can be used to check whether the yacht is dragging if the wind increases.

PORT TRAFFIC SIGNALS Standardised International signals have been agreed and it is expected that they will be introduced at ports as and when the need for change arises. However, the installation of these signals will not be mandatory and they might not be used in every harbour where they might be suitable. (See end Chapter 2.)

Index

Other Stanford Maritime titles on Navigation, Cruising and Seamanship

* In preparation at the time of publication of this book

For a complete list of nautical books, write to the Sales Manager,
Stanford Maritime Ltd, 27a Floral St, London WC2E 9DP